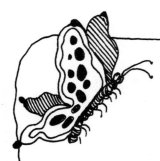

The KIDS' STUFF™
Book of
READING & LANGUAGE ARTS

For The Primary Grades

by Imogene Forte & Joy MacKenzie

Incentive Publications, Inc.
Nashville, Tennessee

Illustrated by Kathleen Bullock
Cover by Susan Eaddy
Edited by Sally Sharpe

ISBN 0-86530-121-2

TABLE OF CONTENTS

COMPREHENSION AND READING INDEPENDENCE

GRAMMAR AND SPELLING

WRITING

DEAR TEACHER OF PRIMARY GRADES STUDENTS,

Primary grades students are very special, indeed. No one knows this better than you! They are eager to learn and are full of energy and enthusiasm, while at the same time they need constant reassurance and encouragement. This means that you have the busy tasks of providing the students with activities that teach basic skills, fostering an excitement for learning, and encouraging students to develop and grow to their fullest potentials.

THE KIDS' STUFF™ BOOK OF READING AND LANGUAGE ARTS FOR THE PRIMARY GRADES was created with your primary students in mind. It contains a rich variety of experiences, both teacher-directed lessons and independent student activities — each structured around an important skill in the language arts curriculum. The stimulating activities have the graphic and thematic appeal needed to capture and hold the attention of primary grades students. Knowing the demands made on today's primary teachers, we have purposely prepared activities that require very little teacher preparation. Each teacher page lists the specific language arts skill, describes any necessary preparation, and outlines each step of the procedure. All of the student pages are ready to reproduce and hand out to the students. This organization and presentation will allow you to spend your time teaching rather than planning and preparing!

This book is packed with creative material to supplement all of your language arts programs:

> speaking and listening
> word recognition and usage
> comprehension and reading independence
> grammar and spelling
> writing

What's more, a study skills chapter gives you 19 exciting activities to sharpen the important study skills necessary for successful learning. In addition, an invaluable appendix contains other useful materials such as word lists, bulletin board ideas, student work sheets, fun ideas, and helpful bibliographies. As a supplement to your basic texts, this will be your most-used reference for teaching reading and language arts!

HOW TO USE THIS BOOK

This book contains six chapters covering the most important areas of the primary language arts curriculum: SPEAKING AND LISTENING, WORD RECOGNITION AND USAGE, COMPREHENSION AND READING INDEPENDENCE, GRAMMAR AND SPELLING, WRITING, and STUDY SKILLS. Within these chapters you will find two kinds of pages. They are:

Teacher Pages — labeled with:

> Each *teacher page* contains a complete plan for a lesson, designed to be directed by the teacher.

*Student pages — labeled with:

> The *student pages* are ready to reproduce and hand to an individual student, a group, or the entire class. These pages can be completed by students with very little or no teacher involvement.

Following these chapters is a carefully planned appendix containing helpful word lists, creative ideas to make books "come alive" for young readers, reproducible forms and work sheets, bulletin boards that teach, and a comprehensive bibliography of wonderful children's books. This section offers the special "extras" that will make your language arts program exciting and interesting for students.

* You have permission to reproduce all student pages and other pages bearing the following statement in quantities suitable for meeting yearly classroom needs:

SPEAKING
AND
LISTENING

TELE-TALK

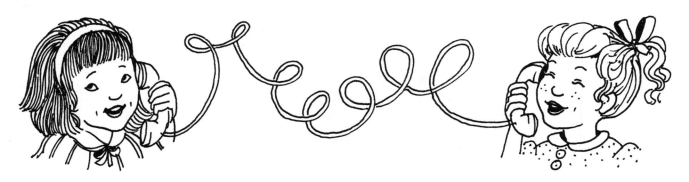

SKILL: Speaking

PREPARATION:
- You will need two telephones (real, toy, or homemade).

PROCEDURE:
1. Explain to the students that each of them will be given an opportunity to engage in an informal, extemporaneous telephone dialogue with another classmate. Each will be pretending to be a fictional character. (Students may or may not choose their partners.)

2. Use the list of ideas below and others of your own to suggest topics for brief exchanges of dialogue between the partners. The students may meet briefly to discuss what they will say, but conversation should not be scripted. Encourage the students to use complete sentences.

Suggestions:
- calling a baby sitter to sit with three sets of twins
- a business person calling for airline reservations
- placing an order for a take-out pizza with six toppings
- a parent calling a school to explain a child's absence
- calling a photo store to see if prints are ready
- calling a pet cemetery to make funeral arrangements for a parakeet
- calling to make a dental appointment
- calling a taxi
- making reservations at a restaurant or hotel
- inviting someone to a birthday party
- calling someone to ask for a dinner date

A HEROIC TALE

SKILL: Speaking

PREPARATION:
- You will need several copies of the mini-drama below and a very abbreviated costume for each player.
  - Maiden - hair bow
  - Maw - apron
  - Paw - beard and/or hat
  - Hero - stick horse and hat

PROCEDURE:
1. Choose four students to be the characters in the tale.
2. Ask the players to read silently as you read the parts aloud to the class. Point out the rhythmic feel of the lines and the similar pattern found in each speaking part. Encourage the players to memorize their lines so they may move freely.
3. Clear a space to create a "stage" for the players.
4. Have the players practice the mini-drama several times. Encourage expressive dramatization, clear enunciation and volume.
5. Let the players perform the tale before the class.

"A Heroic Tale"

Maiden: Help! Help! The bridge is breaking.
I'm going to die . . . I'm going to die!

Maw: Look, Paw! The bridge is breaking.
She's going to die . . . she's going to die!

Paw: Well, Maw, I'll get a ladder.
Hold the bridge . . . hold the bridge!

Maw: Hurry, hurry! I can't hold the bridge.
It's coming down . . . it's coming down!

Hero: (arriving on his horse just in the nick of time)
Let the bridge fall! I'll save the maiden!
Come with me . . . come with me!

Maiden: (as she rides away with the hero)
My hero!

13

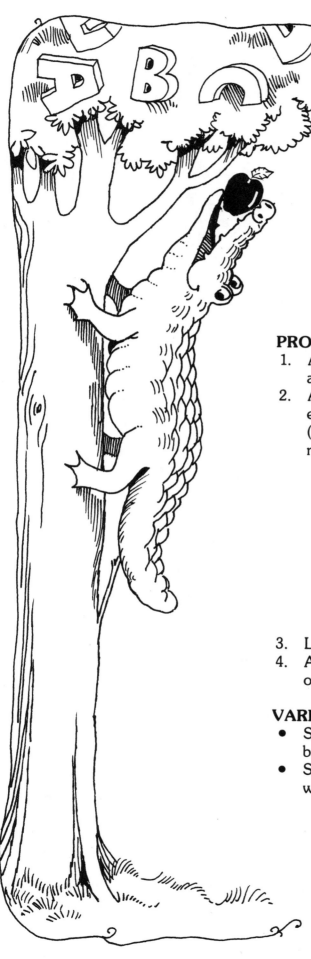

ALPHABET ALLITERATION

SKILL: Speaking

PREPARATION:
- No preparation is required.

PROCEDURE:
1. Assign to each student one or more letters of the alphabet so that all 26 letters are assigned.
2. Ask each student to create a complete sentence in which every word begins with his or her assigned letter. (Encourage the students to use the dictionary and to make the sentences fun and interesting.)

    Example: A - An agile alligator ate apples.
                    P - Polly picks pretty pansies.

    Optional: The articles *a* and *the* may be used freely if desired (see below).

                  The pudgy penguin pillaged the pigeon's pasta.

3. Let the students illustrate their sentences if they like.
4. Ask each student to stand before the class and read his or her sentence(s).

VARIATION:
- Students may create sentences in which every word begins with the first letter of their names.
- Students may write three-word sentences in which every word begins with one of their three initials.

SECRET TALKS

It's made of metal.
It cuts things.
It has handles.

SKILL: Speaking

PREPARATION:
- Collect pictures and/or objects that can be used as subjects for an extemporaneous speaking activity. (You will need at least one object for each student.) Hide the objects from the students.

PROCEDURE:
1. Call one student at a time to the front of the room. Show the student a secret object or picture of an object and give the student three minutes to think of three "sentence clues" which describe the object.
2. Ask the student to share his or her sentence clues with the class. (Students must speak in complete sentences and must not name the objects.)
3. After each student gives his or her clues, ask the class to guess the name of the object.

 # HAPPY HUNTERS

SKILL: Speaking and listening

PREPARATION:
- You will need a tape recorder and several cassette tapes.

PROCEDURE:
1. Plan to have a "hunting party" on a chosen day. Ask each student to choose a small object to hide somewhere in the room.
2. Allow each student to use the tape recorder in private to record directions for finding his or her chosen object. Encourage the students to write their directions before recording them and to choose a familiar "starting place" from which another student may begin the hunt.

    Example: Begin by standing in front of the teacher's desk.
    Take four giant steps toward the windows.
    Turn right.
    Take ten baby steps.
    Kneel on the floor and look straight ahead.

3. Let the students take turns hiding and hunting for objects. Instruct the class to watch as one student at a time follows recorded directions to find an object.

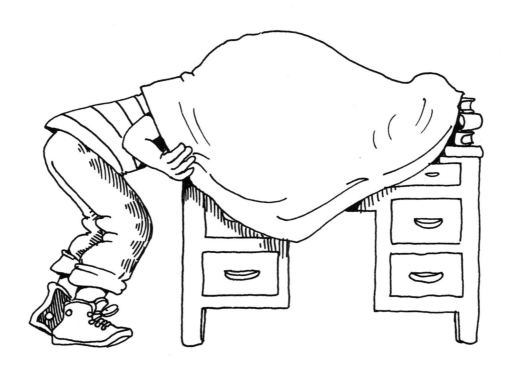

SIX SILLY SAILORS

SKILL: Speaking and listening

PREPARATION:
- Make seven copies of the poem below. On each of six copies, highlight one of the six single-line speaking parts. On the seventh copy, highlight the narrator's part. Distribute the copies to seven students.

PROCEDURE:
1. Let the seven students read the poem once to practice their speaking parts.
2. Ask the students to stand before the class. As the narrator reads the poem, each "sailor" interjects his or her line at the appropriate time. (Encourage the students to use clear enunciation and exaggerated expression.) The "sailors" must run back to their seats upon hearing the word "SPLASH."
3. Have each participant give his or her copy to another classmate. Repeat the activity until each student has participated.

"Six Silly Sailors"
Six silly sailors
Sitting by the sea.
The first one said,
"Something's swimming
   toward me!"
The second one said,
"I think it's a whale!"
The third one said,
"I see a big tail!"
The fourth one said,
"Let's hide in the sand!"
The fifth one said,
"It can't swim on land . . ."
The sixth one said,
"Don't worry; let's stay."
Then SPLASH went the tail
And they all ran away!

MULTI-TOLD TALES

SKILL: Speaking and listening

PREPARATION:
- Ask each student to write the numbers 1-11 down the left margin of a piece of paper.

PROCEDURE:
1. Explain to the students that each of them is to make a list of eleven words by following these dictated directions:

    1. Write the name of an animal.
    2. Write the name of a container.
    3. Write a word you would shout.
    4. Write the name of a strange creature.
    5. Write a verb in past tense.
    6. Write the plural name of an object.
    7. Write the plural name of an object.
    8. Write the plural name of an item of clothing.
    9. Write the name of a street.
    10. Write the name of a body of water.
    11. Write the name of a living thing that moves.

2. After the students have made their lists, distribute copies of the story "All Gone" (page 19). Read the story and ask the students to fill in the blanks with the words they have written.
3. Read the story several times, asking students to stand and fill in the blanks with their words at the appropriate times.

VARIATION:
- Let the students create their own "fill-in-the-blank" stories and directions for word lists to be dictated to friends.

ALL GONE

One fine Tuesday morning, a tiny _____ stuck its head out of a
⟨1. animal⟩

_____ and yelled, " _____ !" A _____, who
⟨2. container⟩ ⟨3. a word you would shout⟩ ⟨4. strange creature⟩

happened to be out for morning exercise, heard the noise and _____ .
⟨5. verb (past tense)⟩

Immediately, the whole town came to life. _____ began to shake,
⟨6. noun object (plural)⟩

_____ began to slide up and down the streets, and a pair of old
⟨7. noun object (plural)⟩

_____ danced down _____ toward the _____ .
⟨8. item of clothing (plural)⟩ ⟨9. street name⟩ ⟨10. body of water⟩

Suddenly, out of nowhere, a huge _____ came along and swallowed
⟨11. living thing that moves⟩

all of them in one monstrous gulp!

THE END

I'm stuffed!

 # CATS

SKILL: Speaking and drama

PREPARATION:
- Gather a group of nursery rhymes and poems about cats (preferably ones that students can recite from memory).

    Examples: Three Kittens Who Lost Their Mittens
    Pussy Cat, Pussy Cat, Where Have You Been?
    Hey Diddle Diddle, The Cat And The Fiddle

- Create a "stage" area large enough to accomodate four or five small groups of performers.

PROCEDURE:
1. Assign a rhyme to a group of two or three students. Ask the students to practice reciting the rhyme in unison using good articulation and expression.
2. Choose an additional student for each group who is to be the actor to pantomime the rhyme.
3. Provide time for the actors and narrators to practice together.
4. Schedule a "show time" and present the rhymes before an audience of classmates or a kindergarten class.

    Optional: Add simple props and costumes, if you like.

VARIATION:
- Choose other topics around which to develop poem cycles. Present the poems in the same manner as outlined above.

PAST, PRESENT & FUTURE

SKILL: Spontaneous oral expression

PREPARATION:
- You will need a large sheet of Manila paper and crayons for each student.

PROCEDURE:
1. Ask each student to fold his or her paper into four equal sections.
2. Give the following instructions:
   - On the first section, draw a picture of one thing you can do of which you are very proud.
   - On the second section, draw a picture of one thing you can do that you could not do last year.
   - On the third section, draw a picture of one thing that you would like to be able to do by this time next year.
   - On the fourth section, draw a picture of one thing you really want to be able to do sometime in the future.

3. Ask the students not to write their names on their papers. Display the drawings on a bulletin board having the title "Past, Present & Future."
4. Ask each student to select one paper and to try to identify the student who drew the pictures by evaluating the achievements and goals illustrated.

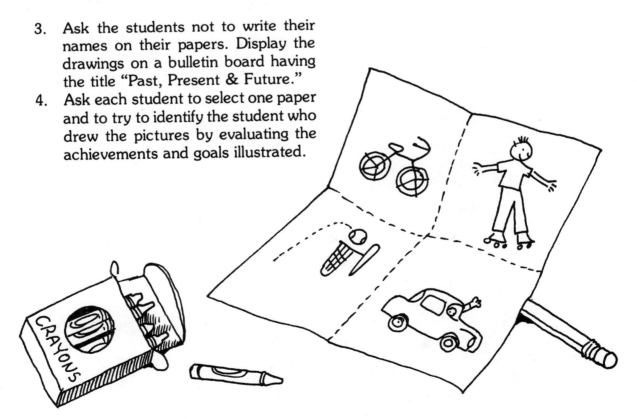

AUTHOR'S DELIGHT

SKILL: Creative oral expression

PREPARATION:
- Gather pictures of children engaged in various activities. Mount the pictures on cardboard or construction paper.
- You will need a tape recorder and microphone for this activity.

PROCEDURE:
1. Share the pictures with the class and let the students discuss what is happening in each picture.
2. Ask each student to choose one picture about which to make up a story or poem. Place the pictures on a bulletin board and give the students several days to look at the pictures and think about their stories.
3. Place a tape recorder and microphone in a quiet corner of the room. Invite each student to bring his or her chosen picture to the corner. After listening to the student's story and making any pertinent suggestions, tape the student as he or she tells the story a second time.
4. After all of the students have recorded their stories, place the tapes in a listening center where students may go to listen to one another's stories.

22

CITY SOUNDS/COUNTRY SOUNDS

SKILL: Critical listening

PREPARATION:
- Prepare a bulletin board display featuring a city scene and a country scene.

PROCEDURE:
1. Lead a discussion about the kinds of sounds one would expect to hear in the city and in the country.
2. Ask the students to lay their heads on their desks, to close their eyes, and to listen as you make a number of different sounds.
3. Ask the students to say "city sound" if the sound they hear would be heard in the city and "country sound" if the sound would be heard in the country.

Examples:

City	Country
siren	cricket
automobile horn	pig
police officer's	duck
whistle	cow
construction	rooster
noises	

4. Let the students take turns making other sounds for classmates to respond to in the same manner.
5. Ask the students to categorize sounds that are pleasant, alarming or frightening, funny, and irritating. Write the categorized words on a chart and place the chart in a creative writing corner to motivate students to write stories, poems, and plays about city and country sounds.

VARIATION:
- Modify this activity by substituting other themes:

    day sounds/night sounds
    inside sounds/outside sounds
    winter sounds/summer sounds

23

 # SOUND OFF

SKILL: Interpretive listening

PREPARATION:
- You will need a drum or a block of wood and a rhythm stick for this activity.

PROCEDURE:
1. Have the students form a circle in a corner of the room. Place a drum or block of wood and a rhythm stick in the center of the circle.
2. Ask the students to discuss words that symbolize sounds.

For example:	bells	sirens
	whistles	feet
	clocks	motors
	clapping	machines

3. Ask each student to select one sound word that he or she especially likes to say.

Examples:	choo-choo	wheee
	boom	bang
	knock-knock	beep-beep
	tick-tock	ah-rumm

4. Instruct each student to quietly whisper the sound word to himself or herself and to "feel" the rhythm of the word.
5. Have volunteers "beat" their sound words on the drum for the other students to guess. As a word is guessed, the students may clap or tap their feet in rhythm with the drummer.
6. Select several words to be listed on the chalkboard. Have one student carry the drum and lead a parade. The other students should march in rhythm and chant the words listed on the board (one at a time).

WORD
RECOGNITION
AND
USAGE

 **SOUND ALIKES**

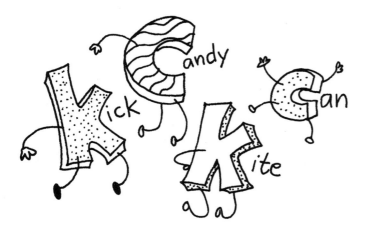

SKILL: Initial consonant sounds

PREPARATION:

Note: The letter *c* and the letter *k* are often used to represent the same sound. The letter *c* is usually used preceding *a*, *o*, and *u*. The letter *k* is usually used preceding *e* and *i*.

- Cut three circles from cardboard (each approximately nine inches in diameter). Cut a triangle (1/6 section of the circle) from two of the circles.

- On both sides of the third circle, draw lines from the center to the edge to divide the circle into six sections as shown.

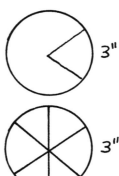

- Stack the three circles, placing the circle with the lines in the middle of the stack. Punch a hole in the center of the stack and connect the circles with a brad to make a wheel.

- Label one side of the wheel *k* and the other side *c*.

- Write the following on the chalkboard:

itchen	ite
at	ute
ey	oat
ut	andy
ettle	andle

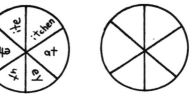

PROCEDURE:

1. Instruct the students to form words by writing the incomplete words on the lines of the circle in the middle of the wheel (on the appropriate side of k or c).

VARIATION:

- Any initial consonants, blends, or digraphs may be substituted for the letters *c* and *k*.

26

BEAT THE CLOCK

SKILL: Initial consonant sounds

PREPARATION:
- Collect several soup or potato chip cans (be sure to clean them). Strip and paint the cans or cover them with construction paper or Contact paper. Use a marker to label each can with one consonant, consonant blend, or consonant digraph.
- Fill a box with mounted pictures (each about two inches square) that represent words beginning with the same sounds as found on the cans.

PROCEDURE:
1. Instruct the students to take turns removing the pictures from the box and putting the pictures in the cans with corresponding beginning sounds.

2. Have a timekeeper watch the clock. The student who is able to complete the activity in the shortest amount of time wins.

VARIATIONS:
- Use several sets of pictures and cans so that several students may compete at one time.
- Each set of pictures and cans may provide practice with a different kind of word classification.

Examples: rhyming words
            prefixes and suffixes
            syllabication

2"

BRANCH OUT

SKILL: Initial consonant sounds

PREPARATION:
- Reproduce the following page for each student.

PROCEDURE:
1. Write a word with a beginning sound that the students need to practice pronouncing in the square at the bottom of the tree.
2. Instruct the students to find pictures in magazines or catalogs with the same beginning sound as the word at the bottom of the tree. Students should cut out the pictures and paste them on the tree branches.

Name _____

BRANCH OUT ✏

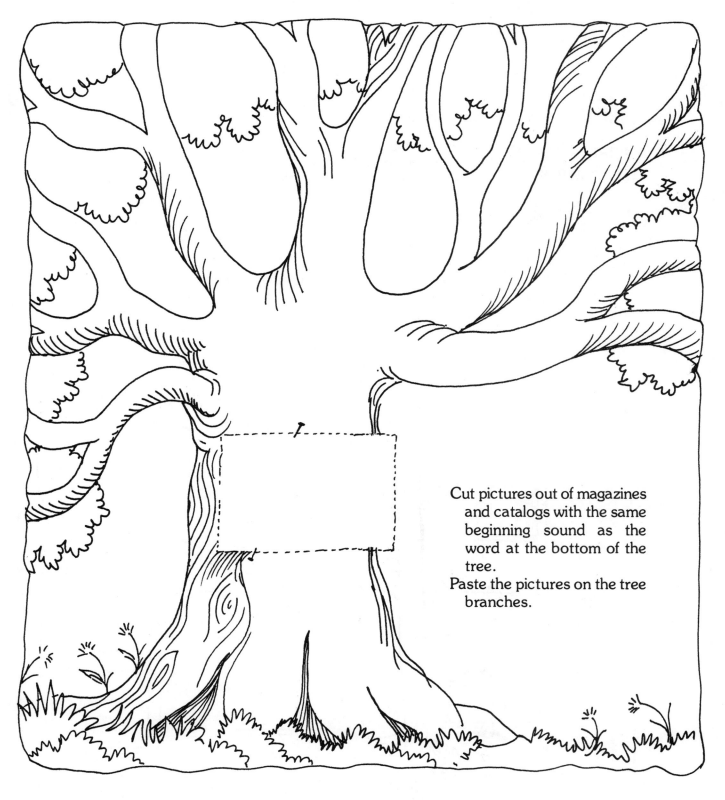

Cut pictures out of magazines and catalogs with the same beginning sound as the word at the bottom of the tree.

Paste the pictures on the tree branches.

Initial consonant sounds
© 1989 by Incentive Publications, Inc., Nashville, TN.

CLIMB

THE LADDER

SKILL: Initial consonant sounds

PREPARATION:
- Reproduce the following page for each student.

PROCEDURE:
1. Have the students write a word on each step of ladder 2 which begins with the same sound as the word on the corresponding step of ladder 1.
2. Read stories such as those by Dr. Seuss and omit rhyming or other "obvious" words so that these may be submitted by students. This provides good practice in "context" thinking.

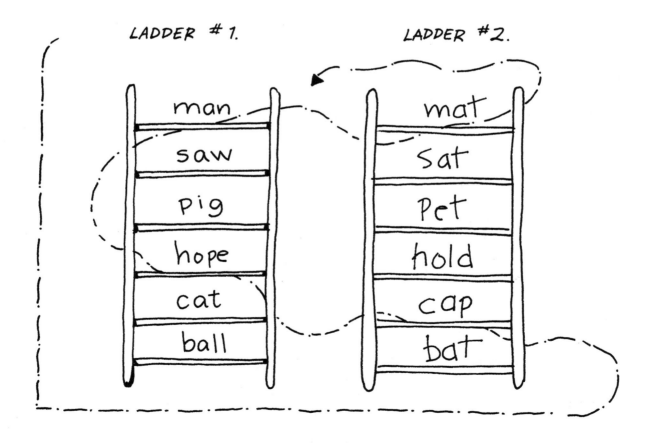

LADDER #1.

LADDER #2.

man	mat
saw	sat
pig	pet
hope	hold
cat	cap
ball	bat

Name ________________________________

CLIMB THE LADDER

Write a word on each step of ladder 2 that begins with the same sound as the word on the corresponding step of ladder 1.

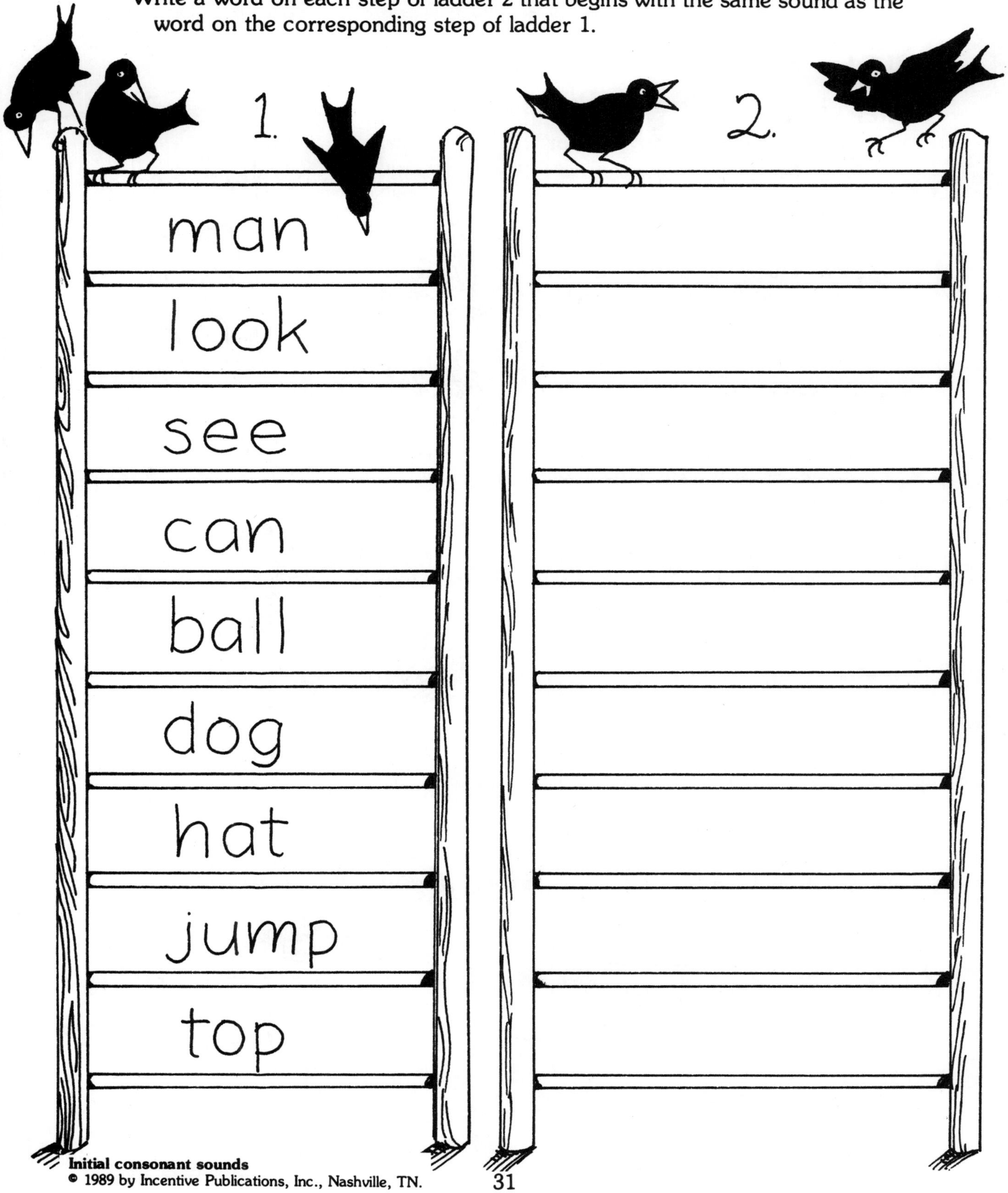
1.
2.
man
look
see
can
ball
dog
hat
jump
top

 # SMART ART

SKILL: Initial consonant sounds

PREPARATION:
- Reproduce the following page for each student.

PROCEDURE:
1. Instruct the students to draw in each square a picture of an object whose name begins with the sound represented by the letter in that square.

VARIATION:
- Divide a bulletin board into squares and write a letter in each square. Have the students draw pictures to tack in the correct squares.

SMART ART

In each square, draw a picture of an object whose name begins
with the sound represented by the letter in that square.

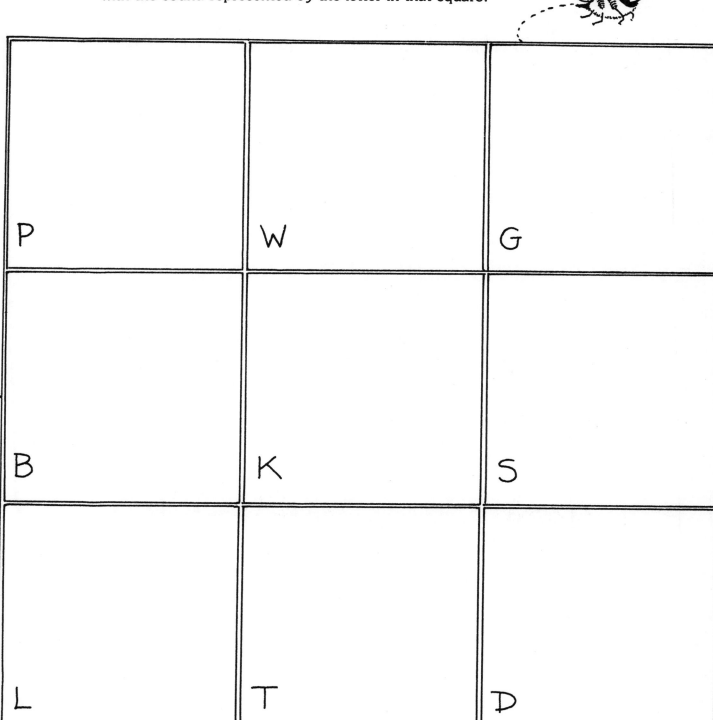

P	W	G
B	K	S
L	T	D

 **WHEEL AROUND**

SKILL: Initial consonant blends

PREPARATION:
- Reproduce the following page for each student. Write an initial consonant blend in the center of the wheel and distribute the pages to the students.

PROCEDURE:
1. Ask each student to write on each spoke of the wheel a word which begins with the sound represented by the blend in the center of the wheel.

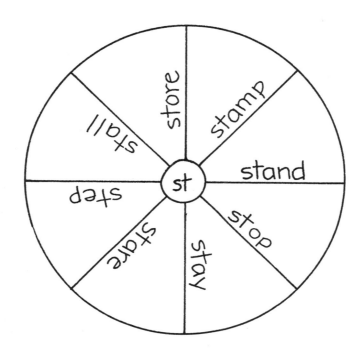

VARIATION:
- Draw a wheel on a large piece of tagboard. Students may list words for the spokes of the wheel and place their lists in an envelope under the wheel. Later, have the class select the words to be written on the spokes.

WHEEL AROUND

Write on each spoke a word which begins with the sound of the blend in the center of the wheel.

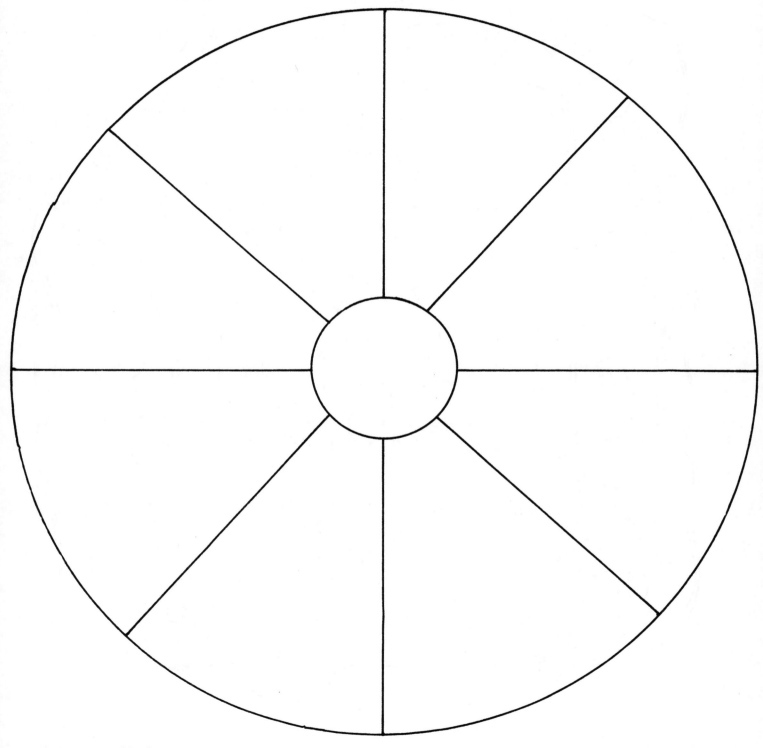

Name _____

/ A FANCY PHONICS FRAME-UP

Color all of the consonants red.
Color all of the vowels yellow.
What a fancy phonics frame-up!

AWAKE OR ASLEEP?

SKILL: Silent letters

PREPARATION:
- Reproduce pages 38 - 40 for each student.
- Write words containing silent letters on the board.

Examples:	night	two	neat	soap	take
	hair	eight	shoe	come	life
	four	sea	lie	toe	boat

PROCEDURE:
1. Ask the students to determine how each of the words on the board is like the others. Students should discover that all of the words contain silent letters (or "sleepy spots"). Ask individual students to underline the silent letters in each word and to say the words.
2. Write words on the board in which every letter is heard (wide awake words).

Examples:	run	me	go	cat	list
	six	ten	it	sink	dog
	bed	test	cry	rap	ship

3. Ask individual students to say the words aloud and to look for "sleepy spots" (silent letters). Students will discover that these words are "wide awake."
4. Hand out the activity pages. Ask each student to cut the page "Are You Awake?" on the dotted lines and to paste each word in its proper category on the other two activity pages.

/ ARE YOU AWAKE?

Cut along the dotted lines.
Paste the words that are "wide awake" (no silent letters) on page 39.
Paste the words that have "sleepy spots" (silent letters) on page 40.

guess	pet
cane	went
Saturday	thing
name	laugh
know	tail
help	year
high	big
friend	fish
can	horse
jump	had
like	family
city	Something

Name _____

WIDE AWAKE WORDS

Paste words that are "wide awake" (have no silent letters) on this page.

Answers on page 239.

WORDS WITH SLEEPY SPOTS

Paste words with "sleepy spots" (silent letters) on this page.

Silent letters
© 1989 by Incentive Publications, Inc., Nashville, TN.

Answers on page 239.

RHYME TIME

SKILL: Rhyming words

PREPARATION:
- Reproduce pages 42 - 44. Paste the pages on poster board and cut along the lines to make cards.

PROCEDURE:
1. Instruct the students to match pictures of objects whose word names rhyme.
2. Ask students to pronounce each pair of rhyming words.

VARIATION:
- During the reading readiness stage, these cards may be used for motivating students in oral language, creative dramatics, and independent seatwork. Encourage students to think of their own "just-for-fun" uses for the cards.

WORD BOX

How Many Syllables?

one	two	three
rock	supper	diamond
back	cafe	bicycle
train	window	elephant
hair	easy	

answers

words

SKILL: Syllabication

PREPARATION:
- Write words having one, two, and three syllables on 3" x 5" cards. Place the cards in a small, flat box. Write the following instructions on a piece of paper to be attached to the top of the box.

Instructions:
Put the words in this box in three columns according to the number of syllables they contain. Put words with one syllable in the first column, words with two syllables in the second column, and words with three syllables in the third column. Then put the words in each row in alphabetical order. Check your work against the answer cards in the envelope attached to the inside of the box top.

- Make an answer card for each "column" and place the cards in an envelope to be taped to the inside of the box top.

PROCEDURE:
1. Place the box in a spot easily accessible to the students for use as a free-time activity.

VARIATION:
- This activity also may be used as a self-checking manipulative bulletin board.

SNIP A SYLLABLE!

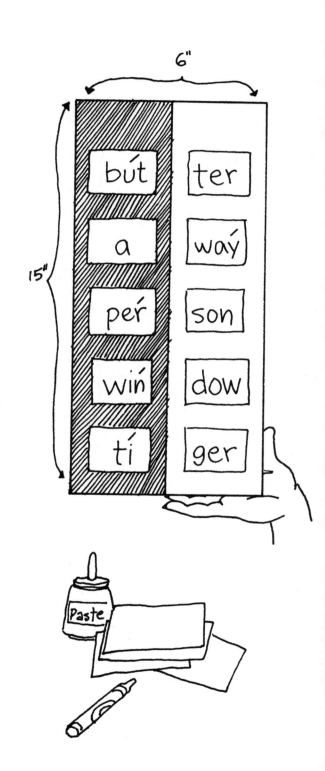

SKILL: Syllabication

PREPARATION:

- Cut a strip of white construction paper approximately 15" long and 6" wide. Cut a strip of colored construction paper 15" long and 3" wide. Paste this strip on the left side of the white paper. Prepare such a "sheet" for each student.
- You will need five 3" x 5" cards for each student. Write a two-syllable word on each card.
- Give each student a prepared sheet, scissors, paste, a crayon, and five 3" x 5" cards.

Note: The words may follow the same pattern (yellow, butter, manner, puppy, etc.), or the words may be of different patterns (yellow, market, away, something, etc.). Follow the procedure which best fits the needs of the students.

PROCEDURE:

1. Ask each student to choose a word card and to cut the card between the two syllables.
2. Instruct the students to paste the first syllable of the word on the colored section of the paper and the second syllable on the white section.
3. Direct the students to use a crayon to place the accent mark in the correct place.
4. Students should continue in this manner until all of the word cards have been pasted on the sheets.

HOW DOES YOUR GARDEN GROW?

SKILL: Root words

PREPARATION:
- Reproduce the following page for each student.

PROCEDURE:
1. Give each student a copy of the activity page. Instruct the students to add letters to the root words to make new words as shown below.

VARIATION:
- Create a learning center disguised as a flower garden for "growing" words. See how many words the students can add! Root words to use for starters might include:

be	I	no	us
he	so	at	we
is	on	as	do

HOW DOES YOUR GARDEN GROW?

Add letters to the root words below to make new words.
Write each new word inside a flower.
Continue adding letters to make new words until every
    flower is filled!

1. IN

2. A

3. AN

4. TO

Root words
© 1989 by Incentive Publications, Inc., Nashville, TN.

WORD ANNEX

SKILL: Prefixes and suffixes

PREPARATION:
- Use a marker to write the following words on pieces of blue felt:

hunt	pay	work	tell
play	slow	like	open
lock	read	teach	

- Write the prefixes *re* and *un* on pieces of pink felt. Write the suffixes *er* and *ly* on pieces of yellow felt.

PROCEDURE:
1. Ask the students to manipulate the words, prefixes, and suffixes on a flannel board to see how many new words they can build.
2. Ask students to give the meaning of each new word.

 WINDOW WATCH

SKILL: Prefixes and suffixes

PREPARATION:
- Cut a piece of tagboard to make a 5" x 8½" board.
- Cut a rectangle out of the center of the board. Make a slit at the top and bottom of the board.
- Write a prefix on a piece of paper and paste it beside the rectangular opening.
- Cut a piece of tagboard 12" long and 3" wide. On this strip write words to which the prefix may be added to make new words.

PROCEDURE:
1. Instruct the students to pull the tagboard strip through the slits and the rectangular window to form words.
2. Have the students pronounce each word, give its meaning, and use it in a sentence.

VARIATION:
- Several of these card games with clearly printed directions make an effective independent activity center.

CHANGE-ABOUTS

SKILL: Prefixes and suffixes

PREPARATION:
- Print each of the words listed below at the top of a sheet of paper. Put the stack of papers in a place which is easily accessible to the students.

help	sing	paint
find	read	laugh
keep	color	cry
send	sleep	try
go	ride	shout
run	fish	give
eat	talk	write

PROCEDURE:
1. Instruct each student to select a word from the stack and to change it in as many ways as possible by adding prefixes and suffixes. (The students may want to use dictionaries for help.)

VARIATION:
- This activity makes a fun group game. Divide students into two teams. Give each team the same words and allow the teams to check orally to find out which team has the most words.

51

QUICK CHANGE

SKILL: Suffixes

PREPARATION:
- Reproduce the following page and give a copy to each student.
- Tell the students to write the title of a unit they are currently studying in the box at the top of the page (for example: winter, community, family, the farm, etc.).

PROCEDURE:
1. Instruct the students to write as many words as possible which are related to the unit and which end in one of the suffixes on the page.

VARIATION:
- This activity can be adapted for group use. Make a large chart and add words each day which are pertinent to a content area.

QUICK CHANGE

Write the title of a unit you are currently studying in the box.
Write as many words as you can that are related to the unit and that end in the suffixes below.

<u>s</u>   <u>ed</u>   <u>ing</u>

Suffixes
© 1989 by Incentive Publications, Inc., Nashville, TN.

Name ______________________________

A STORY TO COMPLETE

Find the missing word ending in the chart below for each blank in the story. Cut and paste the word endings in the correct blanks.

Sally was play________________ (1) with her friend Mary. They were dress________________ (2) their doll________________ (3). Sally had the tall________________ (4) doll. Mary's dolls were small________________ (5).

Sally's little brother came outside. He want________________ (6) to play, too. The girl________________ (7) said, "Go away!" Billy was sad, but he walk________________ (8) away slow________________ (9).

ing	s	ed
est	ed	er
ly	ing	s

Answers on page 239.

SPIN A SENTENCE 🍎

SKILL: Sight vocabulary

PREPARATION:

- Cut a large wheel out of construction paper (approximately 15" - 18" in diameter). Write sight vocabulary words on the wheel. Place the wheel on the left side of a bulletin board.
- Use a small disc of cardboard (6" - 8" in diameter) or a plastic lid (cottage cheese container, etc.) to make a spinner. Attach a construction paper arrow to the disc with a brad. Attach the disc to the center of the large wheel with a small brad or tack.
- Write short sentences containing the sight vocabulary words on a piece of chart paper. Mount the paper on the right-hand side of the bulletin board.

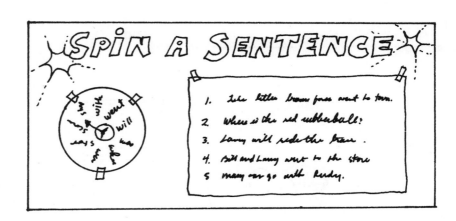

PROCEDURE:

1. Instruct each student to spin the arrow and pronounce the word at which the arrow stops. Ask the student to find the sentence containing that word on the chart and to read it aloud.
2. Change the vocabulary words and sentences periodically.

VARIATION:

- Students may use the board independently by working in pairs.

PICTURE TALK

Decode this message.

      2   2

_____   _____   _____   _____   _____

      U   1

_____ .   _____   _____   _____   _____

4

_____   _____ ?

56

Answers on page 239.

Name _____

STORY OF A STORMY NIGHT

Read the entire story.
Write a word from the word box in each blank to complete the story.

The wind was blowing _____ . _____ roars of thunder
(1)   (2)

and flashes of lightning added to the _____ of the night. How much
(3)

longer could the _____ last?
(4)

Just as everyone had _____ into bed, a _____ knock sounded at
(5)   (6)

the door. Who could be _____ about on a _____ like this?
(7)   (8)

Father _____ the door to reveal an _____ man with a _____
(9)   (10)   (11)

puppy in his arms.

"Please help this _____ puppy," the man said. "I _____ him
(12)   (13)

in a ditch _____ of water and I am _____ he will die if he
(14)   (15)

does not get _____ soon."
(16)

Father was a _____ man, so he said, "Come _____ . We will give the
(17)   (18)

puppy food and _____ . You, sir, are also _____ in our home."
(19)   (20)

Word Box

wildly	wandering	opened	help
settled	welcome	poor	old
night	in	shelter	storm
kind	mighty	afraid	full
loud	excitement	soaked	found

WORD BASKET TURNOVER

SKILL: Contractions

PREPARATION:
- Write contractions on index cards for half of the students in the class.
- Write the pair of words for each contraction on other index cards.
- Choose a student to be "it."

PROCEDURE:
1. Choose a contraction and pronounce it for the class.
2. Ask the two students having the corresponding index cards for that contraction to change seats with one another. As the students change seats, the person who is "it" should try to get one of the seats. The one left standing becomes "it."
3. Continue playing the game until all of the contractions have been chosen.

PLURAL PLACES

Color the shape in each group that names more than one "place."

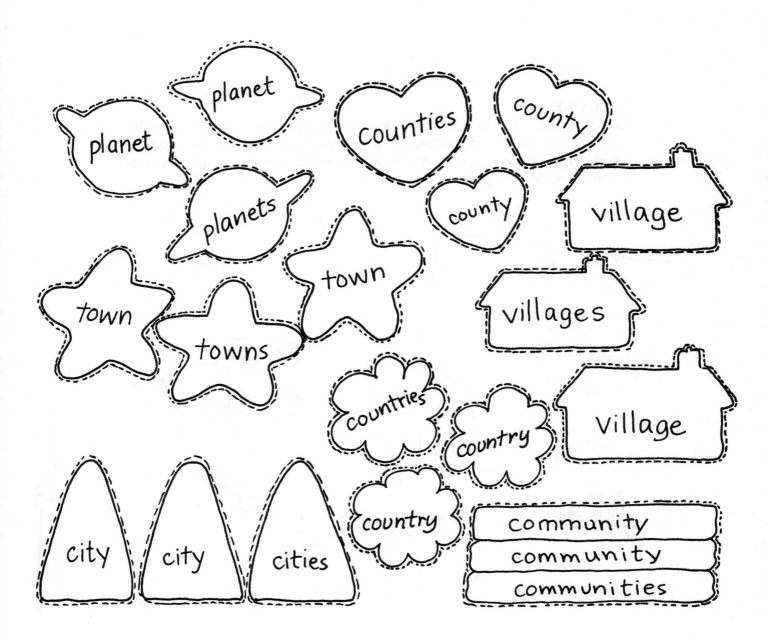

DOUBLE TROUBLE

SKILL: Multiple word meanings

PREPARATION:

• Give each student a 12" x 18" piece of newsprint on which a word has been written.

Suggestions:

trunk	light
match	pen
check	ring
strike	fly
card	plane

PROCEDURE:

1. Direct the students to illustrate various meanings of the words by drawing pictures or cutting and pasting pictures from magazines on the paper.
2. Display the finished papers on a bulletin board having the caption "Words Have Many Meanings."

MATCH-UP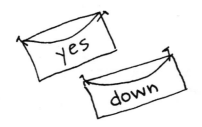

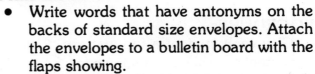

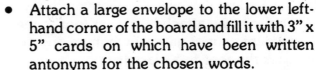

SKILL: Antonyms

PREPARATION:
- Write words that have antonyms on the backs of standard size envelopes. Attach the envelopes to a bulletin board with the flaps showing.
- Attach a large envelope to the lower left-hand corner of the board and fill it with 3" x 5" cards on which have been written antonyms for the chosen words.
- Attach an envelope containing the answer key to the lower right-hand corner of the board.

PROCEDURE:
1. Use the bulletin board as an independent activity. Instruct the students to remove the antonym cards from the envelope in the lower left-hand corner and to place each one in the envelope on which the corresponding antonym is written.

VARIATION:
- This activity may be used for synonyms, homonyms, matching colors, matching sight words, matching shapes, and classifying.

FROM START TO FINISH

SKILL: Homonyms

PREPARATION:
- Construct a bulletin board as shown below.
- Write a special message or class "treat" on an index card. Place the card in an envelope and attach it to the homonym house.
- Cut out one construction paper foot pattern for each student. Write a homonym on each foot.

PROCEDURE:
1. Give each student a foot pattern. Ask one student at a time to use the word in a sentence, to give a homonym for the word, and to use the homonym in a sentence.
2. If a student can give a homonym for the word and correctly use it in a sentence, the student may attach his or her foot to the path leading to the homonym house. If the student cannot give a homonym and correctly use it in a sentence, he or she must pass the foot to a classmate.
3. The students should strive to reach the homonym house by attaching their feet to the path. Upon reaching the homonym house, the students may remove the card from the envelope and read the special message!

Suggested homonyms:

to - two - too
blue - blew
sow - sew
red - read
meet - meat
wait - weight
see - sea
no - know
toe - tow
be - bee
beat - beet
week - weak
tail - tale
fair - fare
hear - here
flour - flower
pair - pear
hare - hair
right - wright
real - reel

GOT IT!

SKILL: Word use in content areas

PREPARATION:
- Prepare vocabulary word cards using words from a unit being studied.

PROCEDURE:
1. Place the stack of cards face down on a table. Let one group of students at a time visit the table.
2. Instruct a student to draw a card from the stack. If the student can pronounce the word, give its meaning, and use it in a sentence, he or she may keep the card. If the student is unable to do all three tasks, any student may say "got it" and claim the card by giving the correct information.
3. The student with the most cards at the end of the game is the winner.

THE GREAT BOOK OF WORDS

SKILL: Word association

PREPARATION:
- Reproduce pages 65 - 69 for each student.

PROCEDURE:
1. Hand out the activity pages. After discussing the titles on the pages, ask the students to think of as many words as they can to write on the pages. (Students may wish to add small illustrations, also.)
2. Combine the completed pages to create a "Great Book of Words." Ask a committee of students to design and make a cover for the book. Add the completed volume to the classroom library. Students may think of additional titles and add pages of their own to the volume.

VARIATION:
- Write appropriate titles or categories on large sheets of white paper and attach them to the bulletin board. Ask students to search through magazines and catalogs for pictures of items that fit each category. As students add pictures to the bulletin board, print the corresponding words on 3" x 5" cards. Place the cards in envelopes, each labeled with the appropriate category. Position the envelopes near the bulletin board and allow the students to go to the board and match the cards and pictures as a free-time activity.

Name _____

List as many loud, giant words as you can.
Add small illustrations, if you like.

LOUD, GIANT WORDS

Word association
© 1989 by Incentive Publications, Inc., Nashville, TN.

Name _____

List as many soft, cuddly "elf" words
as you can.
Add small illustrations, if you like.

SOFT, CUDDLY ELF WORDS

List as many silly, willy-nilly words as you can.
Add small illustrations, if you like.

SILLY, WILLY-NILLY WORDS

Name _____

List as many scary, hari-kari words
   as you can.
Add small illustrations, if you like.

/SCARY, HARI-KARI WORDS

List as many super sad and super serious
   words as you can.
Add small illustrations, if you like.

SUPER SAD & SUPER SERIOUS WORDS

✏ DESCRIBE THE SCENE

Look carefully at the scenes below.
On the lines under each scene, write three
words or phrases from the word list which
best describe that scene.

1. _____

_____

_____

2. _____

_____

_____

3. _____

_____

_____

Word List

eerie
icy and snowy
spring-like
shivery
scary
warm and cheerful
dark and stormy
winter wonderland
bright and beautiful

Answers on page 239.

FEELING FUNNY WORDS

SKILL: Word appreciation

PREPARATION:
- Provide the students with paper and crayons. Write the following list of words on the chalkboard:

scary	strong	square
shaky	long	sick
excited	short	funny
noisy	fat	heavy
tiny	skinny	light
huge	sleepy	bouncy
dizzy	lazy	jumpy
weak	fancy	tall
sad	plain	slippery
happy	angry	wobbly
shy	round	sneaky

PROCEDURE:
1. Instruct the students to use crayons to write the words on their papers in ways that show what the words mean.

VARIATION:
- Use this activity as a bulletin board display. Have the students write words of their own choice on sentence strips to be attached to the board.

🍎 FAMILY FEUD!

SKILL: Vocabulary expansion

PREPARATION:

- Choose five students to represent the heads of five word "families." Give each of these students a 5" x 12" card on which is written the name of the word family.

Examples:

ail   able   and   out   ill

- Make word cards for each word family by writing words "belonging" to the word families on 3" x 5" cards.

Suggestions:

able	ill	and	ail	out
table	trill	stand	hail	pout
cable	chill	band	pail	snout
fable	grill	land	mail	shout
gable	drill	sand	nail	stout
lable	spill	hand	trail	trout

PROCEDURE:

1. Divide the students into five teams.
2. Place the word cards on a chalkboard ledge, making sure there is one card for each student on each team.
3. At a given signal, each student must find one card belonging to the team's word family and line up behind the head of the family. The first team to assemble itself wins.
4. Continue the game by switching the family name signs.

CARD GUMBO

SKILL: Vocabulary expansion

PREPARATION:
- Give each student a card with one of the following words written on it. Write the word beginning with a capital letter on one side of the card and beginning with a lower-case letter on the other side.

the	runs
boy	hops
girl	plays
dog	eats
he	skips
she	goes
it	dances

- Make one card with a period on both sides. Give this card to one student.

PROCEDURE:
1. Ask the student with the word *the* to come to the front of the room. Then have a student with a word that could follow the word *the* come to the front of the room and stand in the correct place.
2. Ask who has a word that could be the third word. Then ask the students what is needed to complete the sentence (a period). Have the student with this card stand in the correct place.
3. Have students continue to substitute nouns and verbs in the proper places in the sentence.

VARIATION:
- Add other words such as tall, big, fat, handsome, softly, a, this, and quickly. Have the students manipulate the cards to discover places these words fit in the sentence.

ALPHABET ANTICS

SKILL: Vocabulary expansion

PREPARATION:
- Prepare a work sheet that has each letter of the alphabet printed on it with space beside each letter. Reproduce the work sheet for each student.

PROCEDURE:
1. Let the class help choose the topic to be used as the title of the work sheet. Instruct the students to write words beginning with each letter of the alphabet which are related to the chosen subject. Let the students choose from subjects such as social studies, science, holidays, sports and other areas of general interest.
2. To make this activity more interesting, include elements related to the chosen theme when preparing the work sheets. For example, use jack-o'-lanterns for a Halloween theme, a border of trains or planes for a travel theme, an easel for an art theme, etc.

SET 'EM UP

SKILL: Vocabulary expansion

PREPARATION:
- Give each student an envelope which contains letters of the alphabet written on 1" x 3½" cards (include several cards for each letter). Be sure to write each letter near the top of the card.
- Give each student a letter holder made from construction paper as shown below.

PROCEDURE:
1. Have the students spell words by placing letter cards in their individual letter holders.
2. This procedure works equally well as an independent activity or as a teacher-directed group activity as outlined below.
   a. Pronounce words for the students to spell in their letter holders and then quickly check each student.
   b. Ask for a word which begins with the same letter as *duck, ball, apple,* etc.
   c. Say the word *jump* and ask the students to place the letter which represents the beginning sound in their letter holders.
   d. Say the words *hit, hop,* and *hip* and ask the students to spell the word which has the short "o" sound.

fold on dotted lines.

 # GREETING GIZMO

SKILL: Vocabulary expansion

PREPARATION:
- Paste used greeting cards on tagboard and cut them apart to make word puzzles that are holiday greetings when put together.

PROCEDURE:
1. Place two or more puzzles in a box labeled "Greeting Gizmo."
2. Ask students to sort and assemble the puzzles in order to read the holiday greetings.

VARIATION:
- The greeting cards may be cut up for use as anagrams. Instruct the students to match like styles of letters.

COMPREHENSION
AND
READING
INDEPENDENCE

✏ RAINY DAY REMEMBRANCE

Study the picture below for several minutes.
Then cover the picture with a sheet of paper and
complete the sentences.
Uncover the picture to check your answers.

1. There are _____ ducks in the pond.

2. _____ ducks are not in the pond.

3. The rabbit is wearing _____ .

4. The big tree is an _____ tree.

5. There are _____ small trees near the pond.

6. The bird has an _____ .

7. A good title for this picture would be _____ .

Comprehension
© 1989 by Incentive Publications, Inc., Nashville, TN.

Answers on page 239.

NEWS FLASH

SKILL: Main idea

PREPARATION:
- Cut articles out of newspapers and separate the headings from the articles.
- Place the articles and headings in a large envelope and print the following instruction on the outside of the envelope:

    Match each heading with the correct article.

PROCEDURE:
1. Place the envelope on a reading table for students to use independently or in small groups as a planned or free-time activity.
2. Ask the students to follow the instruction on the outside of the envelope to complete the activity.

VARIATION:
- The headings may be omitted and the students may write original headings for the articles.

 TITLE TIME

SKILL: Main idea

PREPARATION:
- Cut paragraphs from old textbooks (readers, social studies, science, etc.) and paste them on construction paper.
- Print titles from the paragraphs on index cards or paper strips.
- Make a scrapbook by stapling sheets of plain paper together.
- Place the paragraphs and titles in a shoe box. Paste the following instructions for completing the activity on the inside of the box lid.
  1. Choose a paragraph from the box.
  2. Find its corresponding title.
  3. Paste the paragraph and the title on a page in the scrapbook.
  4. Write a paragraph of your own and a title supporting the main idea of the paragraph on two separate sheets of paper. Contribute these to the box.

PROCEDURE:
1. Instruct students to use the "Title Time" box as a free-time activity or as a group assignment.
2. As new ideas are contributed, the project may retain meaning and student interest for several weeks.

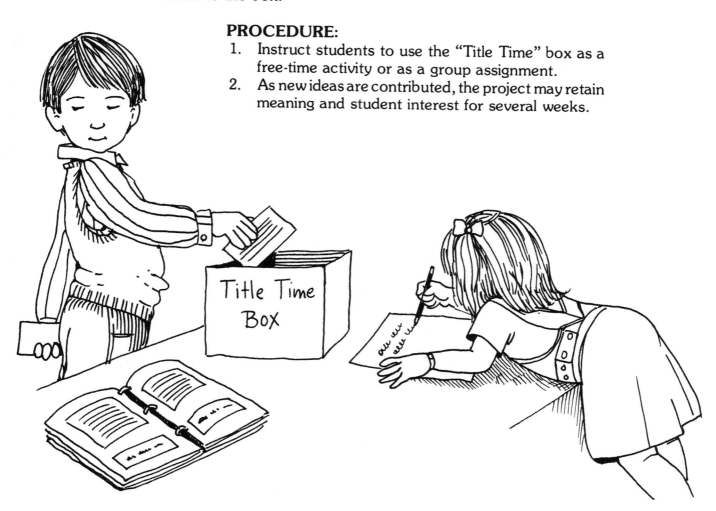

Name _____

NEWSPAPER SURVEY

Select a newspaper from the library or classroom reading table to use in completing this newspaper survey.

1. The full name of the newspaper is _____ .

2. The newspaper is dated _____ .

3. The newspaper has _____ pages.

4. The largest headline on the front page is _____

    _____ .

5. I think this headline story is _____

    _____ .

6. The newspaper's publisher is _____ .

7. Information about the weather is on page _____ .

8. The article that interests me the most is on page _____ .

9. This article is about _____ .

10. The article that I think would be most interesting to my teacher is on

    page _____ .

11. This article is about _____

    _____ .

Facts and details
© 1989 by Incentive Publications, Inc., Nashville, TN.

GO-TOGETHERS

SKILL: Association

PREPARATION:
- Reproduce pages 83 and 84 and paste them on poster board. Cut along the lines to make cards.
- Put the cards in an envelope or box and write the following instruction on the outside of the container:

Pair the cards that "go together."

PROCEDURE:
1. Place the cards on the reading table for students to use as a free-time activity.
2. Instruct the students to shuffle the cards and return them to the container after completing the activity.

VARIATION:
- Give capable students a second set of cards that have the names of the objects printed on them. Ask the students to match the pictures and words.

Name _____

IDIOMATICALLY SPEAKING

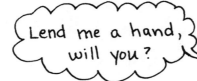

Lend me a hand, will you?

Strain your brain to come up with a brand new, never-heard-before phrase which means the same thing as each sentence below.

1. Lend me a hand, will you? _____

2. I'm in a pretty pickle now. _____

3. He is really in the dumps today. _____

4. My brother gets in my hair. _____

5. It took a lot of elbow grease to clean that carpet. _____

    _____

6. They got into the party by crashing the gate. _____

    _____

7. Having too many irons in the fire will get you in trouble. _____

    _____

8. I was in hot water for arriving late. _____

    _____

9. Do you have a skeleton in your closet? _____

    _____

10. I never see eye to eye with you. _____

    _____

Association
© 1989 by Incentive Publications, Inc., Nashville, TN.

Name _____

✏ A BEAUTIFUL TRAIL

Follow the word trail to the pot of gold at the rainbow's end.

Complete each sentence with a word from the pot of gold.

1. Small animals scurried _____ through the woods.

2. The trees ring with the _____ songs of the birds.

3. The _____ water looked cool and refreshing.

4. The sun sheds a _____ hue over fields and flowers.

5. After the rain, the sky was a _____ blue.

6. The view of the mountains was _____

7. Green grass smells _____ and clean.

oh boy!

joyful breathtaking sweet
golden
brilliant
merrily
sparkling

Association
© 1989 by Incentive Publications, Inc., Nashville, TN.

Answers on page 239.

LET'S GO SHOPPING

Cut out the shopping bag.
Fold along the dotted lines and glue
  the tabs to the back of the bag.
Cut out the objects that you can wear
  and put them in the shopping bag.

Cut out the other items and paste
  them on the outside of the bag.
Tell how you might use each item.

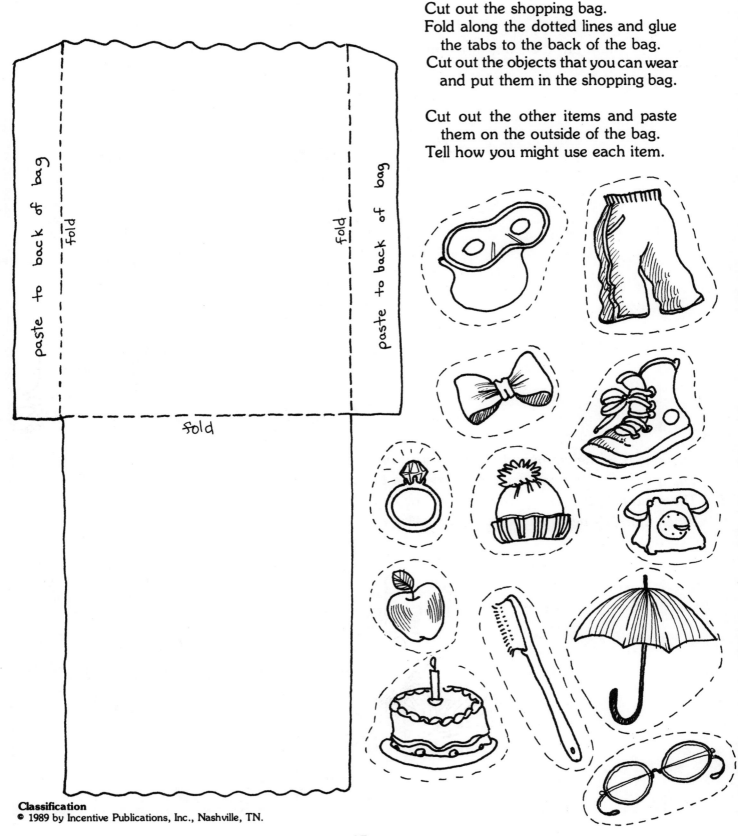

paste to back of bag

fold

fold

paste to back of bag

fold

CLOTHES ON THE LINE

Oh my! Oh my!
Mark out the items in the maid's basket that do not need to be hung to dry.

The king is in the counting house counting out his money,
The queen is in the parlor eating bread and honey,
The maid is in the garden hanging out the clothes,
When along comes a blackbird and nips off her _____ .

tea

Classification
© 1989 by Incentive Publications, Inc., Nashville, TN.

Answers on page 239.

TEMPERATURE CHANGE

SKILL: Classification

PREPARATION:
- Place two pictures on the bulletin board, one illustrating a winter scene and one a summer scene.
- Place word, phrase, or sentence strips pertaining to winter and summer in a large envelope. Tack the envelope to the bulletin board.

PROCEDURE:
1. Instruct the students to remove the strips from the envelope and tack them under the appropriate picture.
2. Attach an envelope to the board which contains an answer card so that students may check themselves.

VARIATIONS:
- For less capable students, place related pictures in the envelope instead of the word, phrase, and sentence strips.
- To adapt the activity for use in a learning center, paste the winter and summer pictures inside a folder. Tape the envelope of pictures or words on the front of the folder and the answer card envelope on the back of the folder.

✏ PASTE IN PLACE

Cut out the pictures below.
Paste each picture in the correct scene.

Answers on page 239.

Name _____

LUCKY TAKES A WALK

Read the story below.
Draw a line to show Lucky's walk.

Lucky will go to the park.
He will see the pond.
He will play with the ducks.
He will hide in the bushes.
He will climb on the bars.
He will smell the flowers.
He will go home.

KEEP OFF THE GRASS

NO DOGS IN PARK

NO WADING

City Park

DO NOT PICK FLOWERS

Sequencing
© 1989 by Incentive Publications, Inc., Nashville, TN.

CUT-UPS

SKILL: Sequencing

PREPARATION:
- Tear stories (appropriate to the students' reading level) out of magazines or old textbooks and cut them into several sections.
- Paste the story sections on heavy construction paper or tagboard.

PROCEDURE:
1. Distribute the story sections to the students so that the students are not aware of who has what story section.
2. Have a student who has the beginning of a story read the story section aloud.
3. Instruct the other students to raise their hands if they think that their story sections should follow the one just read.
4. Have students read their story sections in order until the entire story has been read aloud. Then begin another story.

VARIATION:
- To make this activity more creative and exciting for more able readers, substitute original stories written by the students themselves. The students will enjoy illustrating their story sections, too!

I'm next!

PICTURE BITS

SKILL: Sequencing

PREPARATION:
- Cut the illustrations of well-known stories out of old books or workbooks and mount them on cardboard. Place the illustrations in envelopes to be put on a reading table or the chalkboard ledge.

PROCEDURE:
1. Instruct the students to place the illustrations in proper sequence to tell the story.

ENDING EGG HUNT

SKILL: Sequencing

PREPARATION:
- Print short stories (appropriate for the students' reading level) on construction paper cut in "half-egg" shapes. Omit the endings. Place the unfinished stories in a box on a reading table.
- Write the endings to the stories on the matching "half-eggs." Place these egg halves in another box on the reading table.

PROCEDURE:
1. Give each student a construction paper basket. Instruct the students to match the unfinished stories with the correct endings. Have the students paper clip correctly matched egg halves together and place them in their baskets.
2. When a student has filled his or her basket with the designated number of eggs, the student may invite a classmate to the reading corner to listen to the stories.

VARIATIONS:
- This activity can be used as a party game with each team using one basket to hold the matched eggs. The team with the most eggs wins the game.
- Have the students write original endings for the stories.
- Use this activity as a manipulative bulletin board. Attach a large construction paper basket (with slots for the matched eggs) to the center of the board. Create a border of egg halves with both unfinished stories and story endings. Fill an envelope with paper clips and attach it to the corner of the board for students to use in matching egg halves. Encourage students to go to the board in their free time and select unfinished stories to match with the correct endings.

Note: You may choose to cut several eggs into three sections with three story segments for more capable readers.

RHYME ROUNDUP

SKILL: Sequencing

PREPARATION:
- Reproduce the illustrated nursery rhymes on pages 96 - 98. Cut along the dotted lines to separate the pictures.
- Place each set of illustrations in an envelope labeled with the nursery rhyme title. Put the envelopes in a designated area for an independent activity.

PROCEDURE:
1. Instruct the students to visit the area in their free time. Students may take the pictures from the envelopes and arrange the pictures in the proper sequence.
2. Students will enjoy concluding the activity by telling, writing, or acting out the nursery rhymes (the choice will be determined by the students' maturity level).

I'm so afraid of spiders!

STORY PUZZLE

SKILL: Sequencing

PREPARATION:
- Write each main event of a short, simple story in sentence form on a strip of tagboard. Store the strips in an envelope labeled with the title of the story.

PROCEDURE:
1. Distribute the sentence strips to the students.
2. Have the students work together to arrange the sentences in the correct sequence.
3. Ask the students to reconstruct the story by reading the sentences aloud in the correct order.

VARIATION:
- Use this activity for independent seatwork. Ask the students to arrange the sentence strips in the proper order and to draw pictures to show the story as it happened.

Name _____

✏ WHO, WHAT, WHEN, WHERE

Read the story below.
Circle and label the words or phrases in each sentence that
   tell *who, what, when,* and *where.*
Read carefully!
Every sentence does not tell all of these things.

On this Friday morning Ginny is walking very slowly to school. She kicks

pebbles on the sidewalk as she thinks about last night. She watched two

television programs and talked to her friend Mary on the phone last night. When

the clock struck ten, she remembered that she had not done her homework.

Then her mother told her that the cat had not been fed and that she had not read

a bedtime story to her little brother as she had promised. After feeding the cat

and reading the bedtime story, Ginny had been too sleepy to study. Now, as

Ginny walks to school, she wonders what the teacher will say when he finds out

about her unfinished homework.

Finding details
© 1989 by Incentive Publications, Inc., Nashville, TN.

Answers on page 239.

SUMMARY SAVVY

SKILL: Summarizing

PREPARATION:
- Bring copies of the daily newspaper to class.

PROCEDURE:
1. Ask students to select feature and editorial articles that could become headline stories and to summarize these articles for front page space by rewriting them in three to five sentences. Have the students give the articles new "attention-getting" headlines.
2. As a follow-up activity, ask students to select one school or community event to write as both a feature or editorial article and a front page news story. (Examples: principal's cleanup campaign; winners of the school field day competition; upcoming school carnival; library fund drive; escaped zoo animal; etc.)

Room 12 – Student Newspaper

Principal Cleans Up!

Oct. 12

Mr. Brown, the clean principal

Yesterday, Mr. Brown, principal of Roosevelt school, announced his new campaign to clean up our beloved school......

Eraser

🍎 THINK TANK

SKILL: Mind stretchers

PREPARATION:
- Fill a large cardboard box with mind-stretching activities. Find brain teasers, word find and crossword puzzles, problems to solve, unfinished stories, and "what would you do if . . ." situations in old workbooks and magazines or prepare your own.

PROCEDURE:
1. Place the box on a table which is accessible to the students. Add reference and resource materials to complete a "think tank" to challenge restless and intellectually curious students who always finish first and ask "what's next?"
2. An easy way to add to your "think tank" on a regular basis is to prepare extra copies of required work sheets and student activities to be added to the collection.

Name _____

SUMMER VACATION

Nicole is getting ready for her summer vacation.
The pictures below show what she plans to take with her.
Write words or phrases under each group of pictures to tell what Nicole plans to
    do on vacation.

What do these pictures tell you about Nicole?
Write a brief description of what you think Nicole is like.

_____

_____

/FACTS ABOUT A HOLIDAY

Some of the sentences in the story below state facts.
Some of the sentences state opinions and are not necessarily true.
Underline only the sentences that state facts.

Thanksgiving Day

Thanksgiving Day is a November holiday. I think it is the best holiday of the year. Many families celebrate Thanksgiving by enjoying a special feast. No Thanksgiving dinner is complete without turkey and cranberries. Everyone should eat sweet potatoes, too, because they taste great with turkey. The sweet potato is classified as a root vegetable. My mother's chocolate cake is absolutely the best Thanksgiving dessert in the whole world.

Thanksgiving is always on a Thursday. I think that there should be a holiday that is always celebrated on a Wednesday. Someone should invent a new holiday that lasts two, three, or even four days. I don't think teachers would like that.

There are _____ sentences in the story that state facts.
There are _____ sentences in the story that state opinions.

Fact and opinion
© 1989 by Incentive Publications, Inc., Nashville, TN.

Answers on page 239.

WHO AM I?

SKILL: Character traits

PREPARATION:
- Write the names of well-known characters from favorite stories on index cards. Place the cards in envelopes with the flaps tucked inside.

PROCEDURE:
1. Choose one student to be the "leader" and one student to be "it."
2. Ask the student chosen to be "it" to select an envelope and give it to the leader.
3. The leader draws the card from the envelope and holds it up so that the other students can see it.
4. "It" attempts to find out what character he or she is by asking questions which the other students must answer with yes, no, maybe, or sometimes.
5. When "it" identifies the correct character, he or she chooses the next student to be "it" and then becomes the leader of the game.

105

🍎 IN LIVING COLOR

HOW ABOUT PURPLE?

SKILL: Character traits

PREPARATION:
- Reproduce the following page for each student.

PROCEDURE:
1. Read aloud *Snow White and the Seven Dwarfs* or another fairy tale involving several characters.
2. When discussing the story, ask the students to think about the special traits of each character.
3. Distribute copies of the activity sheet. Instruct the students to list the characters in the character column. After choosing a color which represents the character traits of each character, the student should complete the sentence telling why he or she chose that color.

Example:

Character   Color/Reason
_____   I chose _____ because _____.
_____   I chose _____ because _____.

Note: Other good stories include *The Little Red Hen and the Grain of Wheat, Jack and the Beanstalk, Sleeping Beauty,* and *Hansel and Gretel.*

IN LIVING COLOR

Write a character's name in the blank.
Choose a color which represents the character traits of that character.
Complete the sentence telling why you chose that color.

_____ Character _____	_____ Color/Reason _____
1. _____	I chose _____ because _____
	_____.
2. _____	I chose _____ because _____
	_____.
3. _____	I chose _____ because _____
	_____.
4. _____	I chose _____ because _____
	_____.
5. _____	I chose _____ because _____
	_____.
6. _____	I chose _____ because _____
	_____.
7. _____	I chose _____ because _____
	_____.
8. _____	I chose _____ because _____
	_____.
9. _____	I chose _____ because _____
	_____.
10. _____	I chose _____ because _____
	_____.

Character traits

TRAVEL, INC.

SKILL: Fictional settings

PREPARATION:
- Collect travel brochures from travel agencies.
- Reproduce pages 109 and 110, tape or glue them back to back, and fold as marked to make an example brochure for the class.

PROCEDURE:
1. Ask each student to choose a favorite book he or she has read and enjoyed recently.
2. Ask the students to think about the locations and settings of their chosen stories.
3. Present and discuss the collection of travel brochures. Help the students become acquainted with the methods and techniques used to create a desire in the reader to visit the places advertised.
4. Present and discuss pages 109 and 110 as an example of a brochure created to advertise the location of a favorite fairy tale.
5. Ask each student to create a travel brochure to entice the reader to visit the location of his or her chosen story. Students may use construction paper, felt pens, original drawings, pictures from magazines, maps, etc. to complete their brochures.
6. Allow time for the students to share their brochures with the class. Provide space on the reading table to display the brochures for several days.

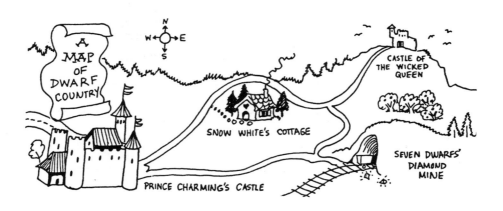

THE ORIGINAL SEVEN DWARFS...

Visit the "HALL of PORTRAITS".
... see the wedding pictures of
Snow White & Prince Charming

fold

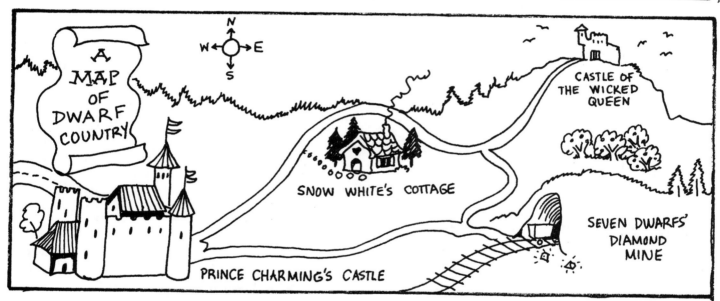

A MAP OF DWARF COUNTRY

N
W E
S

CASTLE OF THE WICKED QUEEN

SNOW WHITE'S COTTAGE

SEVEN DWARFS' DIAMOND MINE

PRINCE CHARMING'S CASTLE

fold

TRAVEL TO WONDERFUL "SUNSHINEY" Dwarf Country

Name _____

VISUALLY SHARP

How "sharp" are you at visualizing images brought to mind by words or phrases?

Read the sentences below and draw the pictures brought to your mind.
Ask a friend to do the same thing on another sheet of paper.
Compare the pictures to see which of you has the most vivid imagination.
Just for fun, act out each of the characters portrayed by your drawings.

Sly Sam was sharp as a whip.

Saintly Sue was so sweet,
sugar wouldn't melt in her mouth.

All the King's horses and all the King's men
couldn't put Humpty together again.

Maria was as angry as an old, wet hen.

TEAR AND TELL

SKILL: Visualizing

PREPARATION:
- No preparation is required.

PROCEDURE:
1. Ask each student to locate a descriptive phrase or passage in a book he or she has read. (Example: "The pink cotton candy was found beside the broken-down Ferris wheel.")
2. Have the students illustrate their selections by making torn-paper illustrations (no scissors allowed).
3. After the students have completed their illustrations, let one student at a time read his or her passage while the other students close their eyes and form mental pictures. Then have the student share his or her torn-paper illustration with the class.

The fuzzy bear flew his kite near a fat white cloud.

ALPHABET TREASURE HUNT

SKILL: Alphabetizing

PREPARATION:
- Arrange word cards (appropriate to the students' reading level) on the chalk ledge.
- Fill a decorative box with plastic letters of the alphabet. (If plastic letters are not available, print the letters on index cards.)

PROCEDURE:
1. Ask a student to draw a letter from the box and to find all of the words on the chalk ledge which begin with that letter. If the student can pronounce the words, he or she may choose the person to take the next turn.
2. Have each student hold the word he or she pronounces correctly until all of the letters have been drawn. Arrange the letters in alphabetical order on the chalk ledge. Ask the students to place their cards in alphabetical order on the chalk ledge at the appropriate time.

 **SHAPE UP!**

SKILL: Following written directions

PREPARATION:
- Tape two pieces of 8½" x 11" cardboard together to make a folder.
- Print these simple directions on the inside of one half of the folder:

  Put the ball in the red ☐ .

  Put the doll in the green ◯ .

  Put the shoe in the blue △ .

  Put the hat in the yellow ☐ .

  Put the coat in the brown △ .

  Put the candy in the black ◯ .

- Reproduce page 115. Cut out the pictures and paste each one on a small card. Place the picture cards in an envelope and tape the envelope beneath the directions inside the folder.
- Reproduce page 116. Cut out the shapes and paste them on the inside of the other half of the folder. Color the shapes according to the directions.

PROCEDURE:
1. For an independent activity, have a student follow the directions to place the pictures in the correct shapes.
2. After completing the activity, each student should return the pictures to the envelope to prepare the activity for the next student.

POT OF GOLD

SKILL: Following written directions

PREPARATION:
- Cut out the clues on the next page and paste each one on a strip of poster board. Place each strip in an envelope and paste each envelope on a large 8½" x 11" envelope.
- Label the envelopes clue 1, clue 2, etc., and put them in different places in the room.
- Cover an 8½" x 11" envelope with gold wrapping paper and write "Pot of Gold" on it. Write special messages to the students on strips of paper and put the messages in the envelope. The messages may be jokes, riddles, or special privileges such as those below.

> You may choose one assignment to eliminate for the day.
>
> You may have five extra minutes of recess.
>
> You may be my special helper tomorrow.
>
> You may choose a friend to play a game with you.

PROCEDURE:
1. Ask a student to draw the clue 1 card and to follow the directions on the card. When the student completes the activity, he or she should place his or her work in the envelope. Direct the student to follow the same procedure for each of the other clues.
2. After a student has completed all ten activities, he or she may draw one slip of paper from the "Pot of Gold" envelope to enjoy a fun message or special privilege.
3. Continue the activity until each student has had a turn.

VARIATION:
- Prepare additional "clues" which require students to complete tasks designed to meet individual learning goals.

Clue 1: Find six compound words in your library books and write them on a piece of paper.

Clue 2: Draw three red apples, a big brown barn, and two little blue hats.

Clue 3: Find five words unfamiliar to you in your social studies book and write their definitions.

Clue 4: Write a letter to an imaginary company to praise one of their products.

Clue 5: Draw a picture of what you plan to be doing ten years from now.

Clue 6: Choose any story book in the class and rewrite the ending.

Clue 7: Find a classmate who wears the same shoe size as you and have him or her sign a piece of paper.

Clue 8: Write instructions directing someone how to get to the cafeteria from your classroom.

Clue 9: Locate your city on a map in the classroom. Write the name of the city or town nearest yours.

Clue 10: Write your name as neatly as you can.

Pot of Gold

This is a different kind of gold!

SIMON SAYS

SKILL: Following written directions

PREPARATION:
- Write sets of directions on 3" x 5" cards which tell how to make or draw things.

PROCEDURE:
1. Distribute the cards to the students with instructions to follow the directions on the cards.
2. After each student has followed the directions on a card, have the students show their final products to the class and explain what was involved in making or drawing the objects. As each student presents a product, the other students should listen to see if the directions were followed correctly.

I can do all of these things easily!

Simon says...
1. Find a piece of yellow construction paper.
2. Cut three circles out of blue construction paper and paste them on the yellow paper.
3. Draw five cats on the yellow paper and color them brown.
4. Cut a square out of orange construction paper. Paste it on the yellow paper.

Simon says...
1. Cut out a picture of a boy from a magazine.
2. Paste the picture on white construction paper three inches from the bottom edge.
3. Draw three trees next to the boy.
4. Draw a tent beside the trees.
5. When you are finished, turn your paper over and draw your teacher.

MIX UP - FIX UP

SKILL: Following written directions

PREPARATION:
- Write sets of directions such as those below:

    Take a sheet of drawing paper from the table in the back of the room.
    Fold the paper into three sections.
    Number the sections 1, 2, and 3.
    Draw a black pony on section 1.
    Draw a red barn on section 2.
    Draw two brown dogs on section 3.
    Cut the sections apart with scissors.

- Write each step of the directions on a card and place the cards in an envelope.

PROCEDURE:
1. Distribute the envelopes to the students and have them arrange the cards in the correct order.
2. Instruct the students to follow the directions on the cards.

VARIATION:
- This activity can be used as a game. Have teams of students work in relays to see which team can correctly arrange a given number of sets of directions in the shortest amount of time.

Fold the paper into 3 sections.

Directions

TWELVE DAYS OF CHRISTMAS

SKILL: Reading appreciation

PREPARATION:
- Cut a large Christmas tree out of green construction paper and another tree of the same size out of white construction paper. Mount the green tree on the white tree and attach the tree to a bulletin board.
- Cut twelve "windows" in the green tree. Number the window flaps from one to twelve. Inside each window, write instructions pertaining to a Christmas book that can be found in the classroom. For example:

Read *The Night Before Christmas* and make a mural showing what happened.

Make up a different ending for *Rudolph The Red-Nosed Reindeer*.

Pretend that you are the angel in the story *The Littlest Angel* and write a paragraph about how you feel.

PROCEDURE:
1. Students will enjoy opening a window each day during the last twelve days before Christmas vacation to find a new experience for each day.
2. Display the students' work on another bulletin board or a project table.

VARIATION:
- Use a book of your choice for other holidays, seasons, or special occasions.

NO PEEKING!

 # FINDERS KEEPERS

SKILL: Reading appreciation

PREPARATION:

- Collect a variety of colorful book jackets and paste each jacket on heavy cardboard. Cut the book jackets into puzzles. (The sizes of the pieces should be determined by the students' maturity level.)
- Place the puzzle pieces for each book jacket in a large envelope or a small, flat box. Label the container with the title and author of the book. Attach instructions for locating the book (in the library or the classroom) to the outside of the container.

PROCEDURE:

1. Instruct the students to work the puzzles and to follow the instructions for finding the books.
2. As a reward, allow the students to check out the books for one night, read the books to other classmates, or read and illustrate the books for a bulletin board display.

GRAMMAR AND SPELLING

Name _____

CAPITAL CLOWN

Circle the words below which should always begin with a
 capital letter.
Write each circled word in its proper form
 on one of the clown's polka-dots.

yes	ocean	lake michigan	dr. seuss
july	court	ohio	mother
mrs.	main street	friday	pippi longstocking
i	africa	united nations	thomas edison
hudson bay	christmas	no	

Capitalization
© 1989 by Incentive Publications, Inc., Nashville, TN.

Answers on page 239.

GRAFFITI FUN

Read each sentence below and decide what punctuation mark is needed to end the sentence. Write each sentence on the proper "punctuation fence" with the correct punctuation.

1. Help, I'm being held prisoner
2. Can you climb this
3. If you can read this, thank a teacher
4. DO NOT write on this fence
5. This sentence was written by a very smart person

6. Danger
7. What's up
8. Is writing on fences legal
9. This side for writers only
10. Keep out

Punctuation
© 1989 by Incentive Publications, Inc., Nashville, TN.

Answers on page 239.

Name _____

MISTAKES IN THE MAILBAG

Something is wrong here!

Postmistress Polly does not like to find mail with mistakes in her mailbag.

Put an X on each envelope that shows an error in capitalization or punctuation.

Then rewrite those addresses correctly on another piece of paper.

(Hint: Four envelopes are perfect!)

M C RICE
Apt. 22
55 Pigeon Rd
Dallas, Texas

Professor U.R. Smart
345 University Square
Hartford, CT

Rev. Hal Hanks
345 Green River Road
Auburn, Alabama

Miss Hansel Hook
444 Cedar street
Gary, Indiana

mrs. Bob Boots
98 Bunny Trail Rd
Columbia, TN

Richard T Jennings
Old Tower trail
Rt 2
Ely, Minnesota

President George Washington
400 Cherry Tree Court
Washington, D.C.

Mr. Steve Potts
3636 High Point Circle
Durham North Carolina

dr John Kit
233 elm St.
Grover, IL

Mr. Ben Hays
804 Water Street
Boston, Ma

miss Beth Jackson
66 river Run
lansing, Michigan

Mr. I.M. Bigg
220 Large Lake Lane
Topeka Kansas

Miss Sara Frank
106 Timber Rd.
Franklin, Ohio

Capitalization & punctuation
© 1989 by Incentive Publications, Inc., Nashville, TN.

Answers on page 239.

THE ELVES' SECRET

Do you know how contractions are made?
Little elves squeeze two words together so tightly that they make one word.
These elves must finish their work before midnight or they will turn into mice!
Help the elves make a contraction out of each pair of words below.

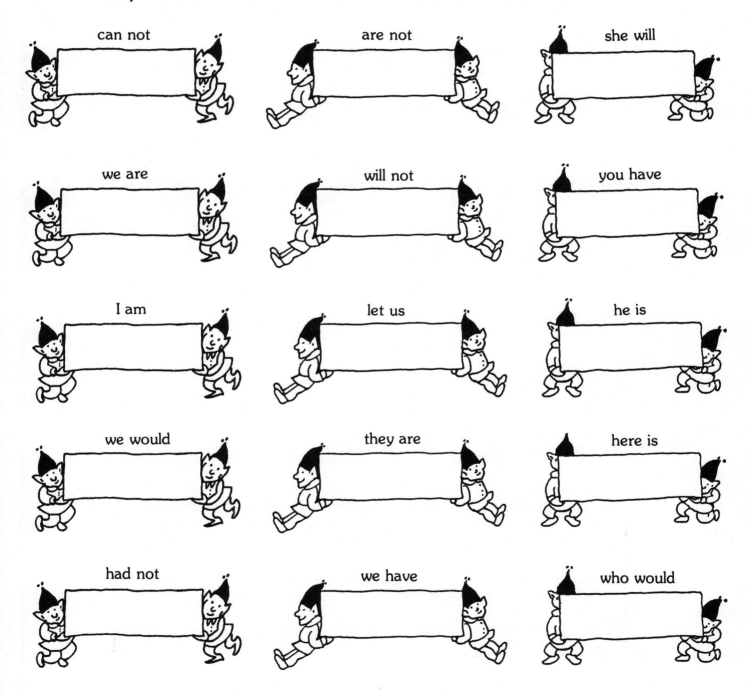

can not

are not

she will

we are

will not

you have

I am

let us

he is

we would

they are

here is

had not

we have

who would

Answers on page 239.

DEALER'S CHOICE

SKILL: Sentence construction

PREPARATION:
- Make a copy of pages 129 - 132 for each student or group of students.

PROCEDURE:
1. Using a set of picture cards, show the students how combinations of the cards may be used to construct sentence stories.
2. Explain that students are to fill blank cards with original phrases and pictures.
3. Students may follow the directions to cut out their own picture cards and create sentence stories.

Note: For more flexibility, the word *and* may be inserted between cards.

DEALER'S CHOICE

Cut out the picture cards on pages 129 - 132.
Choose a card that tells who or what will be the subject of a sentence.
Choose one or more cards that tell what this person or thing does.
Add one or more cards that tell what happens as a result of the action.
Insert the word *and* between cards when necessary.

A ticklish toad

An invisible burglar

A Mexican banana

A shaky shadow

melted into a puddle

floated into
the air

CROWN A NOUN

Color the crowns above the words that are nouns.
Mark through all of the other crowns.

lady

sleepy

king

leader

prince

hungry

pretty

rich

mean

ruler

silly

jester

proud

snob

cross-eyed

queen

Answers on page 239.

Nouns
© 1989 by Incentive Publications, Inc., Nashville, TN.

A VOLUME OF VERBS

A good writer is a collector of wonderful words!
A fun way to keep "in touch" with all kinds of words is to make word booklets.

1. Carefully cut along the solid lines on pages 134 and 135.
2. Stack the pages with the title page on top.
3. Staple the pages together on the left side.
4. Fill each page with words that belong to that group.
5. Add new word groups of your choice to the blank pages.

Continue adding to your "volume" of verbs.
Whenever you write, use it to spark your imagination and to help you write more interesting sentences.

A VOLUME OF VERBS

Name _____

Scary Verbs
devour
stalk

Quiet Verbs
whisper
tiptoe

Loud Verbs
bellow
scream

Friendly Verbs	Dangerous Verbs
smile hug	fall break skid

Sad Verbs	
hurt cry	

Ugly Verbs	
scar hate	

✎ PRIM AND PROPER

A common noun names a person, place or thing.
A proper noun names a *particular* person, place or thing.

Read the nouns below.
Draw a "prim and proper" bow tie beside each proper noun.
Circle each common noun.
Write a common noun below each proper noun which also fits the picture.
Write a proper noun below each common noun which also fits the picture.

Example:

Sam

___boy___

planet

_____

boat

_____

island

_____

Florida

_____

dog

_____

Bozo

_____

Disneyland

_____

street

_____

New York

_____

church

_____

Captain Cook

_____

Answers on page 239.

ADJECTIVE ART

Be an adjective artist!
Read the word list below.
Choose five words to write in "picture language" so that the words "show" their meanings.
Use the back of this page for your artwork.

ADJECTIVES

SKINNY	LARGE	ROUND
FLAT	SLIPPERY	WINDY
OLD	JAGGED	WIGGLY
DAINTY	COLD	LONG
TINY	HAPPY	STICKY
BROKEN	SQUASHED	ROUGH

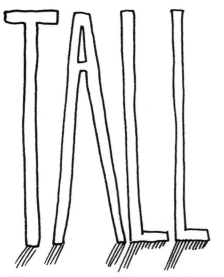

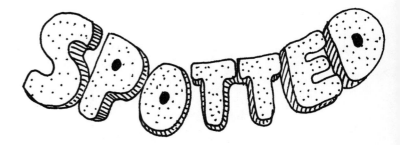

Name _____

✏ NERBS MAKE NEWS!

Nerb is a fun word which describes a word that can be used both as a noun and a verb.
Write a pair of headlines for each nerb below.
Use the word as a noun in the *Morning News*.
Use the word as a verb in the *Evening News*.

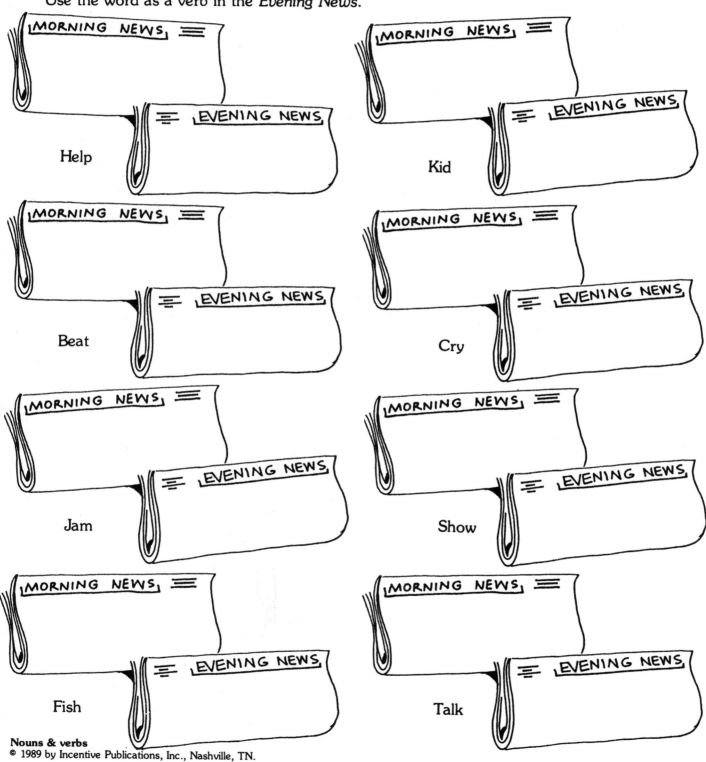

MORNING NEWS

EVENING NEWS

Help

MORNING NEWS

EVENING NEWS

Kid

MORNING NEWS

EVENING NEWS

Beat

MORNING NEWS

EVENING NEWS

Cry

MORNING NEWS

EVENING NEWS

Jam

MORNING NEWS

EVENING NEWS

Show

MORNING NEWS

EVENING NEWS

Fish

MORNING NEWS

EVENING NEWS

Talk

Nouns & verbs

TRIPLE-TREAT VERBS

Treat each object below to a triple helping of unusual verbs.
Look through old magazines to find three unusual verbs that can be added
    to each noun to make a complete thought.
Cut and paste the verbs on the blanks below.
Exchange papers with a classmate to share and enjoy ideas!

🍎 CAT-EGORIZE

SKILL: Parts of speech

PREPARATION:
- Write the following sentences on the chalkboard:

    Ten turkeys honk horns loudly.

    Handsome princes kiss frogs.

    Giggly girls really bother boys.

    Nine dinosaurs dance daintily.

    See silly snails slurping sodas.

    Lizards lick lollipops lazily.

- Reproduce the following page for each student.

PROCEDURE:
1. Have the class read each sentence aloud.
2. Ask the students to categorize each word in the six sentences by writing the word in its proper place on the student page.
3. Encourage the students to use the word groups to create their own sentences.

CAT-EGORIZE

Nouns

CAT

Verbs

SCRATCHES

Categorize every word in the sentences on the board by writing each word on the proper "parts of speech" cat.

Use the word groups to create three new sentences.

Adverbs

HAPPILY

Adjectives

PRETTY

1. ———————————————————————

2. ———————————————————————

3. ———————————————————————

Parts of speech
© 1989 by Incentive Publications, Inc., Nashville, TN.

Answers on page 240.

✏ THREE FOR ONE

Follow these directions for each box below.

Write a noun that names an object on line 1.
Write an adjective that describes the noun on line 2.
Write a verb that tells what the noun does on line 3.
Draw a picture in the box that illustrates the words you have written.

1. _____
2. _____
3. _____

1. _____
2. _____
3. _____

1. _____
2. _____
3. _____

1. _____
2. _____
3. _____

1. _____
2. _____
3. _____

1. _____
2. _____
3. _____

Parts of speech
© 1989 by Incentive Publications, Inc., Nashville, TN.

WHAT'S IN THE BAG?

Fill in the puzzle squares by correctly spelling the name of each picture.

Then read the word in the column below the star to find out what surprise is in the bag.

 # TUMMY TALK

SKILL: Spelling

PREPARATION:
- Cut pieces of string to make necklaces for each student (long enough to hang over a child's stomach). String a colorful cardboard circle (5" - 6" diameter) through each necklace. (Cover the circles with clear adhesive to make them durable.)
- Write a letter from one of the weekly spelling words on each circle. Make enough necklaces to include all letters from the words on the spelling list.

PROCEDURE:
1. Dictate a word. Ask the students wearing the letters in that word to spell the word by placing themselves in the correct order.
2. Continue dictating and spelling words in this manner until all of the words have been spelled.

VARIATIONS:
- Ask each group of students to rearrange themselves to spell as many different words as they can using those letters.
- Write a word on the back of each circle and have the students arrange themselves in alphabetical order, construct a sentence, etc.
- As words are spelled, ask those students representing certain sounds or letters to identify themselves (i.e. vowels, sit down; consonants, stand up; silent letters, cover your mouths).

MAKE MY DAY!

Make the weather man's day!
Fill in the missing letters to spell each "kind"
of day.

1. sn__wy day

2. cl__ __dy day

3. sun__ __ day

4. st__ __my day

5. c__l__ day

6. f__ __gy day

7. d__ __k day

8. __i__dy day

9. r__ __ny day

10. h__t day

Choose your favorite kind of day from the list
above.
Draw and color a picture of that kind of day on
the back of this paper.

What kind of
weather do
you have in
your
area today?

Answers on page 240.

A CLUE OR TWO

SKILL: Spelling

PREPARATION:

- Print spelling words on 5" x 7" index cards. (These words may be from the weekly spelling list, science or social studies units, or other timely sources.)

PROCEDURE:

1. Ask one student to be the "guesser" and to sit facing the group. Choose another student to be the "leader." The leader selects a card and holds it above the guesser's head so that it can be read by the group.
2. The leader calls on group members to give clues about the word by making up riddles or sentences such as those below.

Example: (egg)
   1. The boy found an _____ in the nest.
   2. I had a scrambled _____ for breakfast.
   3. What is oval, white, and fragile?

3. The guesser must say the word and spell it correctly. The student who supplies the clue which enables the guesser to discover the word becomes the next guesser. The guesser becomes the leader.
4. Continue the game until all of the students have had a turn or until all of the cards have been used.

PEBBLES AND PARTNERS

SKILL: Spelling

PREPARATION:
- Gather smooth pebbles and stones (one for each letter for every spelling word).
- Use a permanent marker to write one letter of a spelling word on each pebble.
- Using the pebbles as an anagram, spell each of the words. Be sure all letters are used.
- Put the pebbles in a container to be placed in an independent study center along with a list of the spelling words.

PROCEDURE:
1. Direct the students to visit the center and use the pebbles to practice spelling the list of words. Students may use the list in the envelope for reference.
2. When a student thinks he or she can spell all of the words correctly, the student chooses a partner. The partners take turns dictating words, spelling the words with the pebbles, and checking each other's work.

VARIATION:
- A few extra letters may be added to the group of pebbles to keep the spellers on their toes!

RED IS FOR WRONG

SKILL: Spelling

PREPARATION:
- Write each of the week's spelling words on a 5" x 7" index card. Spell some words correctly and others incorrectly.
- You will need one red and one green sheet of construction paper for each student.

PROCEDURE:
1. Give each student one red and one green sheet of construction paper.
2. Instruct the students to trace one hand on each paper and to cut out the hands. Each student should label the red hand "NO" and the green hand "YES."
3. For a fun group participation review of the weekly spelling words, flash the cards before the group. If the word is spelled correctly, the students should hold up a green hand. If the word is misspelled, students should hold up a red hand.
4. Choose one student to read each word and to spell it aloud correctly.

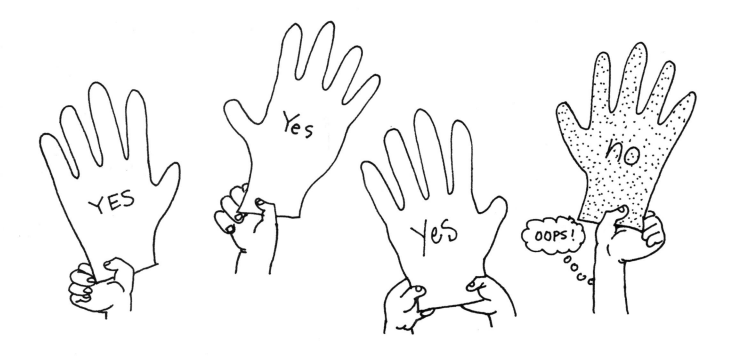

SECRET IN A SACK

SKILL: Spelling

PREPARATION:
- Place each of the following items in a small paper sack: card, corn, car, cork, jar, scarf, marble, fork, yarn, horn.
- Number the sacks 1 - 10 with large numerals.

PROCEDURE:
1. Ask the students to write the numbers 1 - 10 on their papers. Tell the class that the name of the item in each sack contains either the letters *ar* or *or*.
2. Pass the sacks around the room and let the students pinch, smell, or shake the sacks to determine what item is in each sack.
3. Instruct the students to spell the name of the item in each sack beside the number on the paper which corresponds to the number on the sack.

VARIATIONS:
- Other words that follow a spelling pattern may be used such as one syllable words or short *a* words, etc.

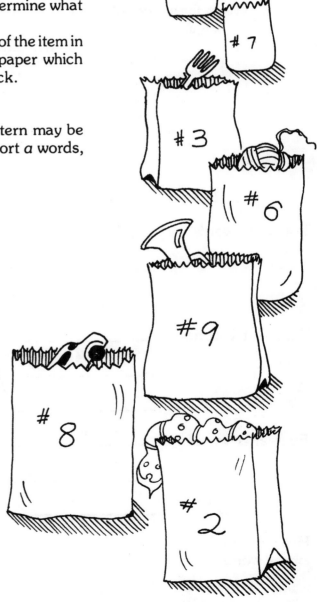

Name _____

HAT MAGIC

See how many words you
can pull out of the hat.
Use the letters in the squares
in any order you wish to
form words.
Write the words in the spaces
below.

Two-letter words _____

_____

Three-letter words _____

_____

Four-letter words _____

_____

Five-letter or
longer words _____

THE PURR-FECT SPELLER

SKILL: Spelling

PREPARATION:
- Record the weekly spelling words on cassette tape.
- Place a list of the spelling words, written in the same order as on the tape, in a large envelope.
- Reproduce several of each kind of badge on the following page and place the badges in the envelope with safety pins.
- Reproduce page 153 and paste it on the outside of the envelope.
- Place the envelope in a study center with the cassette tape and a tape recorder.

PROCEDURE:
1. Have students visit the study center and follow the directions on the envelope to prepare for a spelling test.
2. Discuss the possible uses of the badges and explain that anyone who chooses a HELP badge will be assigned a spelling "buddy" to help him or her prepare for the test.

PURR-FECT SPELLER

Here's how to make a perfect grade in spelling this week!

1. Read the study rules below and use them as you prepare for the spelling test.
2. Listen to the cassette tape. Write each spelling word as it is pronounced.
3. After writing every word, remove the word list from this envelope and check your spelling.
4. Choose the badge in the envelope that best describes what kind of speller you are and pin it on with a safety pin.

Note: If you choose the HELP badge, your teacher will assign a spelling "buddy" to help you.

HOW TO STUDY A SPELLING WORD

1. Look carefully at the word.
2. Say the word aloud, pronouncing each syllable carefully.
3. Think about the word's meaning.
4. Shut your eyes and try to picture the word in your mind.
5. Look at the word and write it, saying each letter as you write.
6. Write the word again without looking at the list.
7. Check to see if you have spelled the word correctly.
8. Repeat these steps until you have mastered each word.

🍎 CONNECT-A-WORD

SKILL: Spelling

PREPARATION:
- Make a large chart such as the one on this page and attach it to a bulletin board.
- Put yarn, a pair of scissors, and straight pins in an envelope and attach the envelope to the board.
- Write the following instructions below the chart:

> Cut lengths of yarn and pin the yarn on the board to connect letters to spell a word. The yarn may not cross a letter that is not part of the word. When you have connected as many words as possible, copy your words on a sheet of paper. Return the yarn, scissors, and pins to the envelope for the next person.

PROCEDURE:
1. Use the bulletin board as a free-time activity. Encourage students to go to the board independently or in small groups.
2. Have the students hand in their word lists and check them to see who found the most words.

VARIATION:
- Turn the bulletin board into a reproducible student activity. Copy the chart on paper and reproduce it for the students. Instruct the students to connect letters to spell words by drawing lines with their pencils. (A line may not cross a letter that is not part of the word.)

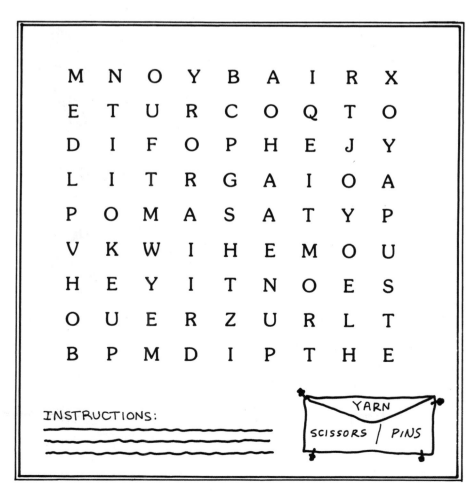

M	N	O	Y	B	A	I	R	X
E	T	U	R	C	O	Q	T	O
D	I	F	O	P	H	E	J	Y
L	I	T	R	G	A	I	O	A
P	O	M	A	S	A	T	Y	P
V	K	W	I	H	E	M	O	U
H	E	Y	I	T	N	O	E	S
O	U	E	R	Z	U	R	L	T
B	P	M	D	I	P	T	H	E

INSTRUCTIONS:

YARN
SCISSORS / PINS

154

WRITING

BEWARE THE WORD WIPER

SKILL: Word choices

PREPARATION:
- Ask each student to bring a large, smooth rock to class.
- Provide the students with markers that will write on rocks.
- Use a large box and black construction paper to make a secret cave in which the rocks may be hidden.

PROCEDURE:
1. Ask the students to pretend that a monstrous "Word Wiper" carrying a giant eraser is roaming the earth. The Word Wiper uses the giant eraser to erase words from books, papers, signs, cards, and magazines. He even erases words from remote places such as the tops of light bulbs, watch faces, and labels inside clothing. Every word in the world will soon be erased forever. Only words that are "carved" in stone and hidden in a secret cave can be saved from the Word Wiper's eraser.
2. Inform the students that each person in the world can save only his or her five favorite words. Each student must decide what five words he or she will save and why.
3. When each student has chosen five favorite words, he or she should use a marker to write the words (in large letters) on a rock. Have the students hide their rocks in the cave.
4. Students may take turns sharing their five favorite words at a later time. Encourage each student to visit the cave and "read" the rocks during his or her free time.

WORD WALL

SKILL: Vocabulary development

PREPARATION:
- Use butcher paper to cover a wall in the classroom.
- Provide the students with colorful markers.

PROCEDURE:
1. Explain to the students that they are to "collect" new words to develop their writing vocabularies.
2. Ask each student to "discover" two to four new words or phrases to add to his or her writing vocabulary. The student must be able to define each word and tell why he or she chose it.
3. Have the students use colorful markers to write their words on the wall in large, neat letters. (The students might enjoy illustrating the words.)
4. After every student has contributed, read, define, and "share" the words. At a later time, assign a writing activity which involves the use of the word wall.

VARIATION:
- Specify a special classification of words: part of speech, theme, words related to a given content area, etc.

✏ WEB OF WORDS

Choose five to ten words from the web and use them to "weave" a scary story.

You may add endings such as *ed, s, es, ing,* and *er* to the words as necessary.

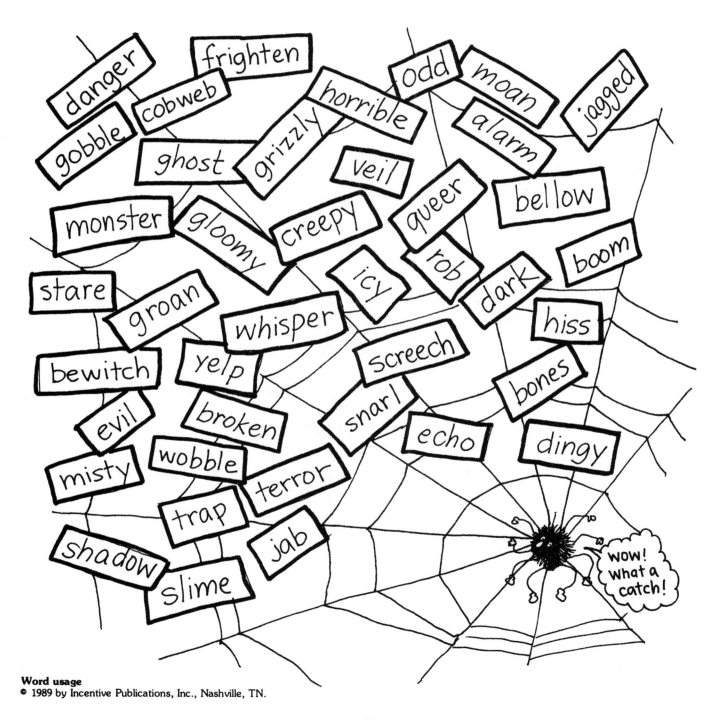

Word usage
© 1989 by Incentive Publications, Inc., Nashville, TN.

158

NEW ADDITIONS

SKILL: Sentence construction

PREPARATION:
- Divide the class into two evenly-numbered teams.

PROCEDURE:
1. Ask the first person on each team to make up a three-word sentence and to recite the sentence loudly and clearly.
2. Instruct the second person on the team to use the same three words and a fourth word to make up a new sentence. (The new word may be added anywhere in the sentence.) The student then recites the four-word sentence.
3. Direct the third person on the team to use the same four words and a fifth word to expand the sentence again. The game continues in this manner until every team member has had a turn. If a team member is unable to create a sentence using all of the previously used words, he or she loses that turn. The team with the longest sentence wins.

BORROWED WORDS

SKILL: Using writing resources

PREPARATION:
- Gather a number of old magazines.
- Tear from the magazines one page of appropriate reading material for each student.
- Each student will need one sheet of 12" x 18" construction paper.

PROCEDURE:
1. Distribute the construction paper and magazine pages to the students.
2. Ask the students to fold the construction paper in half to form a "booklet."
3. Have each student paste the magazine page on the inside left-hand page of the booklet. On the opposite page, the student should paste one piece of writing paper.
4. Ask the students to read silently as much of their magazine pages as they can and to think how they might use many of the words to write a mini-story on the opposite page. (Students also may use words not on the magazine pages.)
5. After completing their stories, the students should underline each word "borrowed" from a magazine page.

AIR-BORNE IDEAS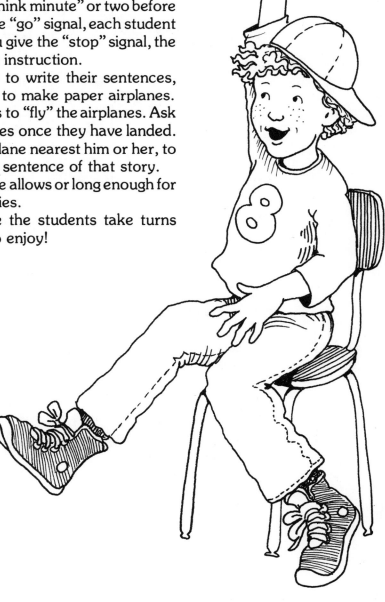

SKILL: Story sequence

PREPARATION:
- Each student will need one sheet of paper and a pencil.

PROCEDURE:
1. Students should have paper and pencil ready so that they can write the opening sentence of a great story at a given signal. Explain that you will give them a "think minute" or two before giving the signal. When you give the "go" signal, each student is to write one sentence. When you give the "stop" signal, the students are to listen for the next instruction.
2. After the students have had time to write their sentences, instruct them to fold their papers to make paper airplanes.
3. Give a signal directing the students to "fly" the airplanes. Ask the students not to touch the planes once they have landed.
4. Ask each student to pick up the plane nearest him or her, to unfold it, and to write the second sentence of that story.
5. Continue in this way as long as time allows or long enough for the students to develop their stories.
6. After the last airplane toss, have the students take turns reading the stories aloud for all to enjoy!

DREAM THEME

SKILL: Story sequence

PREPARATION:
- Create an out-of-sequence copy of the sentences on the following page and reproduce it for each student, or scramble the sentences as you write them on the chalkboard.

PROCEDURE:
1. Explain to the students that the sentences are part of a dream sequence.
2. Ask the students to read the sentences silently.
3. Work as a group to sequence and number the sentences. (Note: There is no one perfect sequence. The story needs only to make dream-like sense.)
4. When all of the sentences have been numbered, read the dream sequence aloud.
5. Encourage the students to create dream sequences of their own to trade with friends.

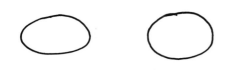

Dream Sequence

You are walking to school.

You notice a dark figure lurking behind a tree.

Suddenly, someone jumps out at you.

You try to run, but your legs won't work.

You are kidnapped.

You faint.

You wake up in a tunnel.

You find a rope.

It is tied to something you cannot see.

You follow it.

You are attacked by a crocodile.

You faint.

When you awaken, you are crossing a river
  on the crocodile's back.

You see a child clinging to a floating log.

You rescue him.

You try to stop a passing boat by waving at it.

You are rescued.

Your mom hugs you.

The mother of the rescued child hugs you.

The President calls to congratulate you.

✏ SHOES ARE CLUES

You can tell a lot about a person by looking at his or her favorite shoes.
Look at each shoe below and think of words that would describe its
  owner.
Write the words on the shoe.

THE AWESOME APPLE

SKILL: Description

PREPARATION:
- Give each student an apple and a copy of the following page.

PROCEDURE:
1. Ask the students to display their apples on their desks.
2. Instruct the students to feel, smell, taste, and look at their apples. Ask the students to think of words they might use to describe their apples.
3. Discuss any questions on the student page that the students find difficult to read or understand. Then let the students follow the directions to complete the page.

Name _____

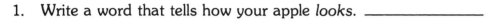 # THE AWESOME APPLE

1. Write a word that tells how your apple *looks*. _____

2. Write a word that tells how your apple *smells*. _____

3. Write a word that tells how your apple *feels* in your hands.

    _____

4. Take a bite of your apple. Did you hear a sound?

    Write the sound word. _____

5. How does the apple taste? Write a taste word. _____

6. Look at the place where you bit the apple.
    Notice the shape of the bite.
    Name something that might have this shape. _____

7. Name three special dishes that can be made from apples.

    _____

8. Think of three ways an apple may be used other than as a food.

    _____

    _____

    _____

9. If apples did not have a name, what name would you call this fruit?

    _____

10. Does an apple remind you of something that is not food?

    Tell what and why. _____

11. Enjoy eating your apple!

Description
© 1989 by Incentive Publications, Inc., Nashville, TN.

PEOPLE STEEPLE

SKILL: Description

PREPARATION:
- Provide each student with crayons, markers, glue, construction paper and a rectangular box.

PROCEDURE:
1. Ask each student to think about the VIPs (very important people) in his or her life. Have the student write on a piece of scrap paper all of the words or phrases he or she can think of that describe those people.
2. Work together to make a composite list of descriptive words and phrases. Write the list on the chalkboard.
3. Ask each student to choose a VIP in his or her life and to decorate the four sides of a box as follows:

Side 1: Write the name of the VIP and his or her relationship to you. (Examples: Mrs. Tom Branch, grandmother; Mr. Ed Howe, coach; Miss Judy Moore, piano teacher.)

Side 2: Write two words that describe the character of the VIP. (Examples: kind and generous; tough and demanding; smart and talented.)

Side 3: Write a phrase or sentence that tells how you feel about this person. (Examples: "I always feel comfortable with her." "He makes me do my best." "She likes me even when I don't like myself.")

Side 4: Draw a picture of the VIP, or glue a photograph of the VIP on the box.

4. Encourage the students to incorporate their own styles into the decoration of their boxes.
5. Stack the completed boxes, placing the largest box on the bottom and decreasing in size to the top, to create a "people steeple" of VIPs.
6. Invite others to view the people steeple and enjoy the descriptions.

NOTE: This is an excellent idea for parents' night or open house!

BALLOON TALK

These two pages will give you practice in writing direct quotations.
Write in the "talk balloons" to create a conversation between the characters in each
  block.
The conversation may be silly or serious.
Be sure to use correct punctuation.

Dialogue
© 1989 by Incentive Publications, Inc., Nashville, TN.

Name _____

PIECE OF MIND

Look at each picture below and imagine what thought the child might be thinking.
Write the thought in the "think balloon."

Writing drama
© 1989 by Incentive Publications, Inc., Nashville, TN.

✏ CAUGHT!

1. Cut along the solid lines and staple along the dotted lines to make a tiny book.
2. Read the title of the book, write your name on the line beside "author," and draw an illustration on the cover.
3. Look at each drawing and imagine what it would be like to be the "caught" character in that picture.
4. Write a mini-story of at least three sentences for each picture. Give each mini-story a title.

Prose/narrative
© 1989 by Incentive Publications, Inc., Nashville, TN.

✏ BEASTLY BIOGRAPHY

Look at the picture and think of a good name for this funny beast.
Then write a story that tells about the beast's
  beginning, habits, or adventures.
Share your story with classmates.

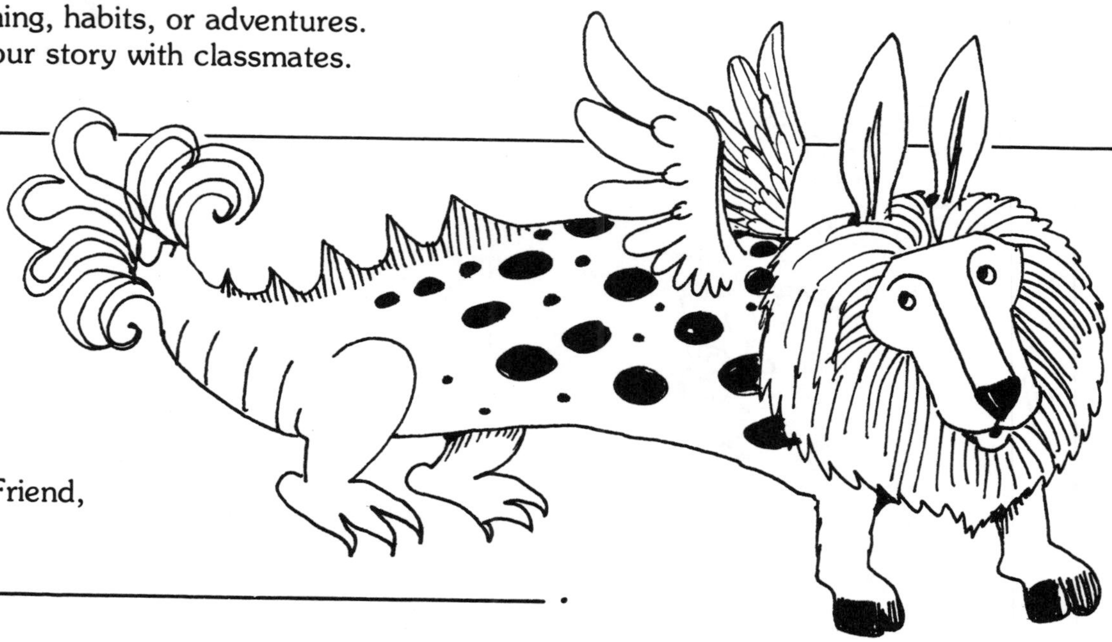

Meet My Friend,

_____ .

_____

_____

_____

_____

_____

_____

_____

_____

Prose/narrative
© 1989 by Incentive Publications, Inc., Nashville, TN.

CREATE A CRAZY-IKE

SKILL: Prose/fantasy

PREPARATION:
- Gather old magazines, scissors, paste, large sheets of construction paper and pencils.
- Prepare two or three Crazy-Ikes to be used as examples (see instructions on the following page).
- Mount the student instructions on tagboard to make a study guide.
- Place the materials in an interest center.
- Prepare a bulletin board near the interest center where students may display their finished products. Caption the board "CRAZY-IKES IN CAPTIVITY!"

PROCEDURE:
1. Introduce the center to the students by reviewing the instructions and showing examples of Crazy-Ikes.
2. Ask the students to visit the center, to compose their own Crazy-Ikes with accompanying stories, and to add them to the bulletin board.

How To Create A Crazy-Ike

1. Cut out two or three magazine pictures and glue them together to create an absolutely crazy, "couldn't-be-true" picture.
   Examples:
   - a dog driving a car with feet instead of wheels
   - a cat with wings wearing a bonnet
   - a rabbit with a peacock's tail

2. Mount your Crazy-Ike on the top half of a sheet of construction paper.
3. Write a story about your Crazy-Ike. Try to make the story funny and to give it a surprise ending.
4. After writing your story, copy it in neat handwriting beneath your Crazy-Ike.
5. Add your picture and story to the Crazy-Ike bulletin board.

Mike, The Crazy-Ike Dog

One day Mike was running down the street in his new, four-footed car. Suddenly, he had a flat foot, so he pulled into Dr. Toes' Foot Repair Garage. "Are your dogs barking?" laughed Dr. Toes. "That's a joke. Ha, ha."

Name _____

EYEWITNESS

Look carefully at the picture below.
Ask yourself these questions:

WHO is taking part in the action?　　WHEN is it happening?
WHAT is happening?　　　　　　　　WHERE is it happening?

Answer the questions in the boxes below.

Who?	What ?

Where?	When ?

Imagine that you are the only person who saw this event take place.
You must describe what happened to the police and a news reporter.
Write your report below.
Be sure to include all of the facts — no opinions, please!

_____

_____

_____

Reporting
© 1989 by Incentive Publications, Inc., Nashville, TN.

JUST DROPPING A LINE TO SAY

SKILL: Writing letters

PREPARATION:
- Address an envelope to each of the characters listed on the following page. (Add others your students would enjoy and subtract those that may be inappropriate.) Place the envelopes in a box.
- Make a "mailbox" to hold the finished letters.

PROCEDURE:
1. Explain to the students that they are going to have the opportunity to communicate with some very famous literary characters.
2. Read the names of the characters aloud so that the students can begin to imagine the possibilities for interesting letters.
3. Have each student choose a favorite character and write a letter (in proper form) telling or asking the character whatever he or she chooses. Students may give advice or tell how they would have behaved differently to change the story.
4. When all of the letters have been mailed, redistribute the letters so that each can be answered. Allow the students to volunteer to "be" specific characters, or distribute the letters randomly (making sure no student has his or her own letter).

5. At a later time, the students may read their letters and responses aloud. Display the letters in a writing center or on a bulletin board for all to enjoy.

Dear Grinch,

What a despicable character you are! Every kid in the world turns gray-green when your name is mentioned! How did you get to be so mean? Your folks must not have brought you up right....

Here are some other great Characters:

Jack And The Beanstalk
The Wizard Of Oz
Little Red Riding Hood
Snow White
The Very Hungry Caterpillar
The Ugly Duckling
Corduroy
Stuart Little
Eloise
Paddington
Frog And Toad
Nate The Great
Lyle, Crocodile
The Grinch Who Stole Christmas
Ping
Jimmy's Boa
Madeline

The Velveteen Rabbit
Amelia Bedelia
Curious George
Ralph S. Mouse
Clifford, The Big Red Dog
The Gingerbread Boy
Cinderella
Sara Sylvia Cynthia Stout
Tom Thumb
The Cat In The Hat
Pippi Longstocking
Little Bo Peep
Gentle Ben
Ramona Quimby
Heidi
Homer Price
Winnie The Pooh

The Grinch
10 Gloomy Place Way
Somewhere Else

Name _____

✏ SILLY SING-SONGS

Write a rhyming word in each blank to make ten silly poems.

An Easter egg
On a chicken _____ .

Onion skin
With a golden _____ .

A piece of fruit
In a cowboy _____ .

A movie star
In a racing _____ .

A doggie bone
In an ice-cream _____ .

A rosy peach
On a sandy _____ .

A bashful fox
With his head in a _____
_____ .

An apple pie
With an open _____ .

A silly cat
In a lady's _____ .

A helpless cook
On a fishing _____ .

Now, write two silly poems of your own.

1. _____
   _____

2. _____
   _____

PICTURE POETRY

This is a picture poem about things that go.

Cut out the pictures below and paste them on another sheet of paper to make a
   picture poem about animals.
Find the two pictures that rhyme.
Use one of the rhyming pictures at the end of line two and the other rhyming
   picture at the end of line four.

On the back of the paper, draw a picture poem of your very own!

Poetry/rhymed couplets
© 1989 by Incentive Publications, Inc., Nashville, TN.

A IS FOR ALPHABET

SKILL: Unrhymed poetry

PREPARATION:
- Write the sample poems on the following page, or similar poems of your own, on a chart or chalkboard.
- Prepare a large cut-out letter of the alphabet for each student. (Plan to give the most difficult letters to the most able students.)

PROCEDURE:
1. Ask the students to read the sample poems with you. Discuss how the key letter is used in each poem. (The object is to use key letters as many times as possible.)
2. Distribute one alphabet letter to each student.
3. Ask the students to use a dictionary and scrap paper to collect ideas for their poems. Instruct the students to plan and write rough drafts of their poems.
4. When each student is ready, he or she may copy the poem on a large cut-out letter.
5. Designate a time when students may share their poems with the class. Display the letters on a wall or bulletin board for all to enjoy.

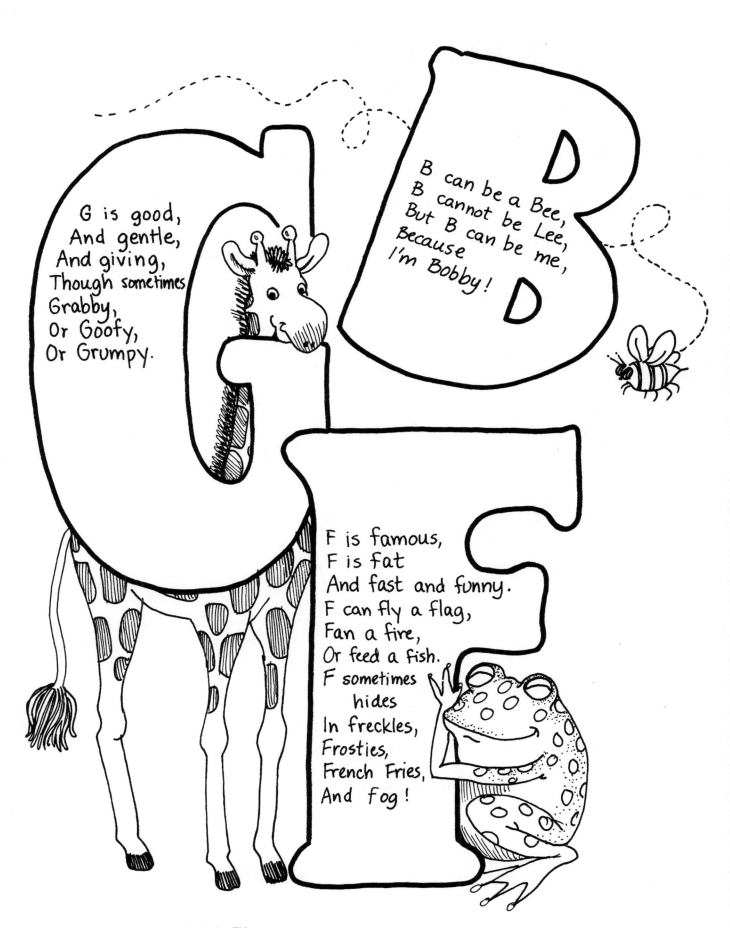

G is good,
And gentle,
And giving,
Though sometimes
Grabby,
Or Goofy,
Or Grumpy.

B can be a Bee,
B cannot be Lee,
But B can be me,
Because
I'm Bobby!

F is famous,
F is fat
And fast and funny.
F can fly a flag,
Fan a fire,
Or feed a fish.
F sometimes
    hides
In freckles,
Frosties,
French Fries,
And fog!

POEM CLUSTERS

SKILL: Poetry on a theme

PREPARATION:

- Collect or compose a group of simple poems, each related to the same theme. Copy the poems on a picture or shape symbolic of the theme and group the shapes on a poster or bulletin board.
- Enlarge the weather symbols below to use for student-composed poem clusters. Reproduce several of each of the small symbols on which students will write poems.

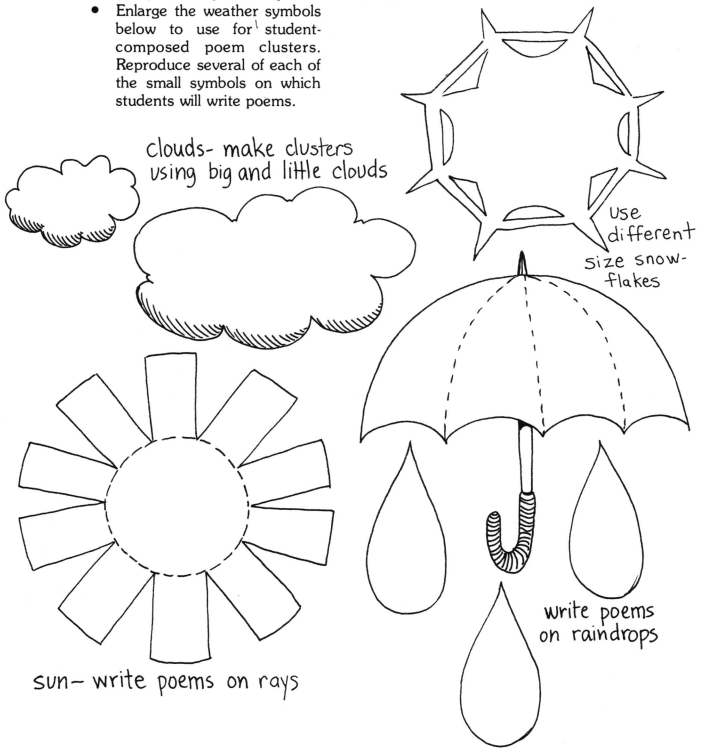

clouds- make clusters using big and little clouds

use different size snow-flakes

sun— write poems on rays

write poems on raindrops

PROCEDURE:

1. Share and enjoy the poem cluster you have created with the class. Explain that a poem cluster is a group of poems, collected or original, that relate to a given theme.
2. Discuss a variety of themes that would be easy to use for poem clusters.
3. Think of poems or songs the students might know which are related to the four weather-related symbols. Show the symbols to the class.
4. Place each of the four symbols on a large poster or bulletin board and ask the students to collect as many poems as possible for each one by copying poetry from books or from memory, or by composing new ones.
5. As students collect their poems, ask them to write the poems on pictures or symbols related to each theme. Group poems of like theme around the appropriate large symbol on the poster or bulletin board.
6. Read the poem clusters aloud together and discuss the feelings, imagery, sounds, rhymes and rhythms as appropriate to the interests and ages of the students.

VARIATION:

- Assign groups of three or four students to create a poem cluster.

Suggested Themes:

legs	the sea	noisy things
animals	scary things	the color blue
feelings	nonsense stuff	peculiar people
friends	things that go	

/ WEATHER WISHES

If you could have just one weather wish, what would it be?
What kind of weather do you like best?
What kind of weather do you wish would never be?
Write a poem about the weather.

(The poem may or may not rhyme.)

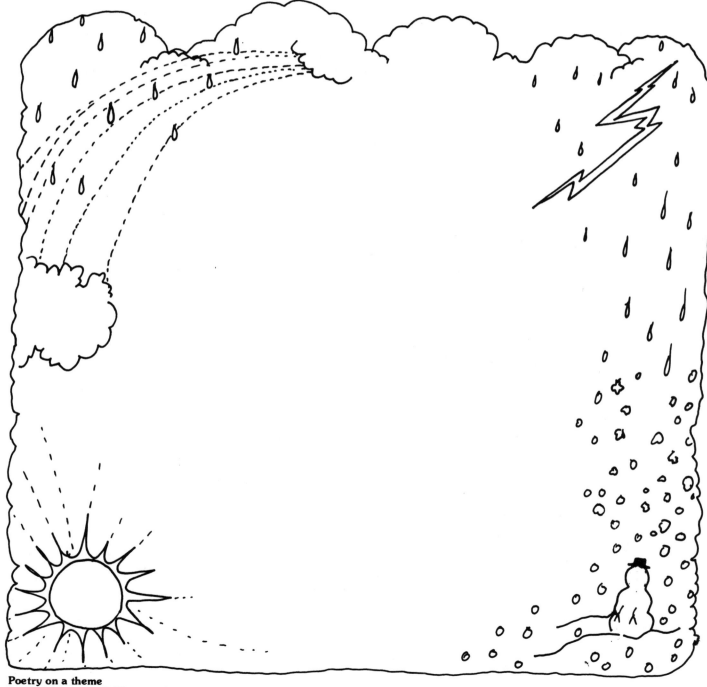

HIGH-CLASS CUISINE

SKILL: Writing directions

PREPARATION:
- Gather a variety of cookbooks and make them available for browsing. (Children's cookbooks are especially appropriate.)
- Supply the students with construction paper.

PROCEDURE:
1. Encourage the students to spend time browsing through the cookbooks. Ask the students to pay particular attention to how the directions are written.
2. Initiate a class discussion about the "how-to" format of a cookbook. List qualities that make following and understanding cookbooks easy for the reader (i.e. list form, illustrations, short sentences, step-by-step directions, etc.).
3. Explain that the students' task will be to create a class cookbook. Ask each student to supply one simple, easy-to-follow recipe.
4. Instruct the students to write their recipes on scrap paper so that you may approve them.
5. After approving the recipes, have each student copy and illustrate his or her recipe on construction paper.
6. Combine all of the recipes to make a class cookbook for the reading table. Encourage students to copy recipes they would like to try at home.
7. On an appointed day, ask each student to bring from home a "taste" of his or her recipe to share with the class.

TITLE DEPOSITORY

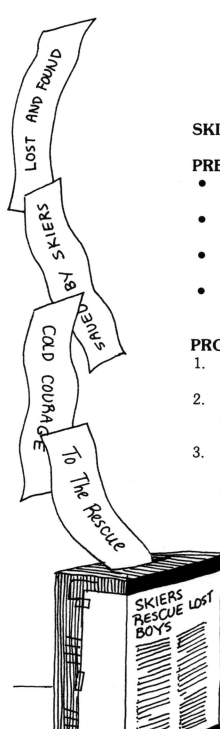

SKILL: Writing titles

PREPARATION:
- Collect several empty cereal boxes and cover each with construction paper.
- Choose several highly-motivating one-page articles from magazines appropriate to the students' ages and interests.
- Paste one article on the face of each covered box and cut a slot in the box top.
- Place the boxes in a learning center with a stack of six-inch strips of paper.

PROCEDURE:
1. Ask the students to visit the center and to read one or more of the articles.
2. When a student completes an article, he or she must write a good title for the article and his or her initials on the back of a paper strip and deposit the strip in the box.
3. After each student has had the opportunity to visit the center, open the boxes and let the class review and evaluate the titles given to the articles.

BILLBOARD BOULEVARD

BE A SPORT—
and make
a
basket !

WASTE BASKET

DON'T LITTER

SKILL: Writing captions

PREPARATION:
- You will need several bulletin boards or large pieces of poster board, a variety of art supplies, and plenty of work space.

PROCEDURE:
1. Ask the students to identify and describe billboards they have seen along the highway. Discuss what the billboards have in common (large type; few words; attention-grabbers; colorful; persuasive — try to get people interested in a product, service, place or activity).
2. Divide the class into groups of three or four students.
3. Ask each group to plan and create a billboard that will attract classmates to a product, service, place or activity.
4. Remind the students to choose words carefully and to make the billboards eye-catching and attractive.

VARIATION:
- The class may create billboards for the school hallways to advertise special school activities or events.

LET ME OUT! LET ME OUT!

SKILL: Personification

PREPARATION:
- Prepare a "mystery box" for each student by placing a common object in a small box, or have each student bring a "mystery box" from home.

PROCEDURE:
1. Give a mystery box to each student (or have the students trade boxes so that each has a box containing an object unknown to him or her).
2. Instruct the students to use their five senses to ascertain the contents of their mystery boxes (opening the boxes is not allowed!). When a student thinks he or she knows what is in the box, he or she may write a story in first person, imagining that he or she is the object inside the box.
3. Let each student read his or her story to the class, a partner or a small group. After reading the story, the student may open the box to reveal the hidden object. Even the authors will be surprised at the findings!

LOST

This is a picture of lost and unclaimed objects found in a classroom at
the end of the school year.

Each of these objects has a story.

Choose one object and write its "story" to explain how it came to such
a lonesome end.

P.S. 21 — LOST and FOUND

Peter
Rabbit

COMICS

Teacher's
Guide
Notes

Name _____

✏ HOLD YOUR TONGUE!

She's driving me up the wall!

If you believed the sentences below were exactly true, someone might think you were crazy!

Each sentence has a meaning different from its exact or literal meaning.

These sentences are called idioms.

Choose one idiom.

Draw an illustration of its silly (literal) meaning.

Write a sentence that explains its real (intended) meaning.

He blew his stack.
Lend me a hand.
I'm in hot water!
He's in the doghouse!
He bit the dust!
She's full of baloney.

I jumped right out of my skin!
They crashed the party.
She's walking on clouds.
It's raining cats and dogs.
Hold your tongue.
He's tied to his mother's apron strings.

Silly Meaning

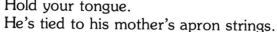

Real Meaning

_____

RUMPER STICKERS

Bumper stickers are for cars and trucks.
Rumper stickers are for people!

Choose three people in the school for whom
you would like to make a rumper sticker.

Use crayons or markers to write creative, witty, and wise sayings on
the strips below (do not write hurtful or rude sayings).

Cut out the stickers and present them in person!

Eye nevur make
spelling miztakes

Caution: I
brake for RECESS

QUIET! Mind in
Operation

1.

2.

3.

Simple literary devices
© 1989 by Incentive Publications, Inc., Nashville, TN.

Name _____

PINT-SIZE STORIES BY PINT-SIZE PEOPLE

It's fun to make-believe that you can shrink to a very small size and fit into some unusual places.
Write a very short, pint-size story from each of these unusual places.

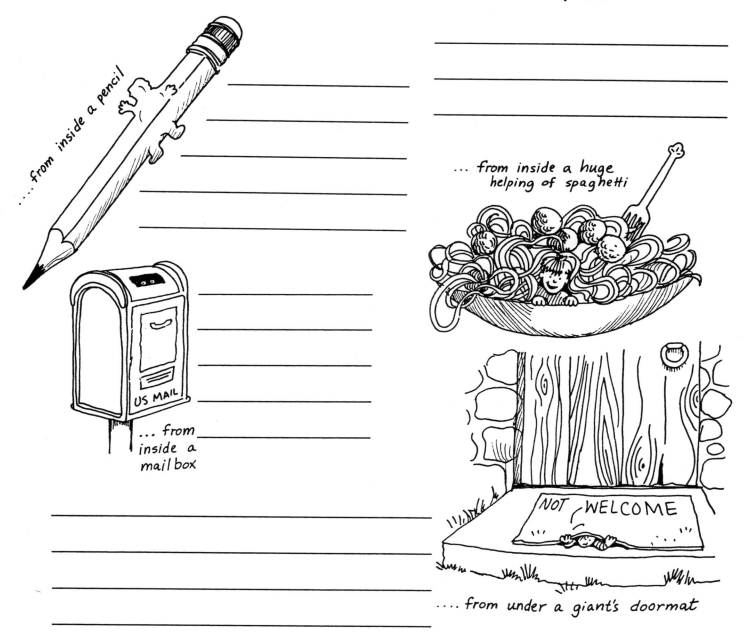

... from inside a pencil

... from inside a huge helping of spaghetti

... from inside a mail box

.... from under a giant's doormat

NOT WELCOME

US MAIL

Think of one other strange or unusual place from which you would like to write, and write another pint-size story on the back of this page.

Point of view
© 1989 by Incentive Publications, Inc., Nashville, TN.

STUDY SKILLS

PICTIONARY PASTE-UP

Cut out the picture cards below.
Say the word name for each picture.
Then say the word name for each picture on page 197.
Alphabetize the picture cards by pasting them in the correct picture boxes on page 197.
Be sure the word name for each picture falls between the picture "guide words" in the correct box.
Use a dictionary if you need help.

Dictionary skills/alphabetization
© 1989 by Incentive Publications, Inc., Nashville, TN.

Name _____

Answers on page 240.

Name _____

✏ FAMILY AFFAIR

A group of names, words, or ideas that have something in common can be called a *family*.
Use a dictionary and encyclopedia to find the family name for each group.
Write the family names in the blanks provided.

Example: corn, broccoli, peas, carrots   *vegetables*

1. gram, ton, quart, liter, bushel _____

2. Boston, Denver, Chicago, Clearwater _____

3. Snake, Ganges, Danube, Amazon _____

4. mandolin, oboe, tympani, euphonium _____

5. Thomas Edison, Alexander Bell, Jonas Salk, Eli Whitney _____

6. wheelbarrow, shovel, trowel, hoe _____

7. Babe Ruth, Sonja Henie, O.J. Simpson, Billie Jean King _____

8. New Zealand, Nigeria, Belgium, Peru _____

9. Claude Monet, Norman Rockwell, Pablo Picasso _____

10. triangle, rhombus, heptagon, diamond _____

11. John F. Kennedy, Abraham Lincoln, Ronald Reagan, Lyndon Johnson _____

12. Alberta, Ontario, Prince Edward Island, British Columbia _____

13. Atlantic, Indian, Pacific, Arctic _____

14. Sydney, Perth, Melbourne, Brisbane _____

Bonus: George Washington, Alan Shepard, Jr., Adam and Eve, Sandra Day O'Connor

_____

Dictionary/encyclopedia skills
© 1989 by Incentive Publications, Inc., Nashville, TN.

Answers on page 240.

Name _____

TROPICAL SAFARI

There are 12 animals hiding in this picture of a tropical rain forest.
Find and color each animal.
List the animals you find in the blanks below.

Animals I found:

1. _____   7. _____

2. _____   8. _____

3. _____   9. _____

4. _____   10. _____

5. _____   11. _____

6. _____   12. _____

Look up "tropical rain forest" in an encyclopedia to find out more about tropical animal life.

Encyclopedia skills
© 1989 by Incentive Publications, Inc., Nashville, TN.

Answers on page 240.

HOME, SWEET HOME

Cut out the pictures below.
Paste each child and his or her home beside the correct country or continent on
    page 201.
Then color the pictures.
If you need help, use an encyclopedia to locate the name of the country or
    continent.

Name _____

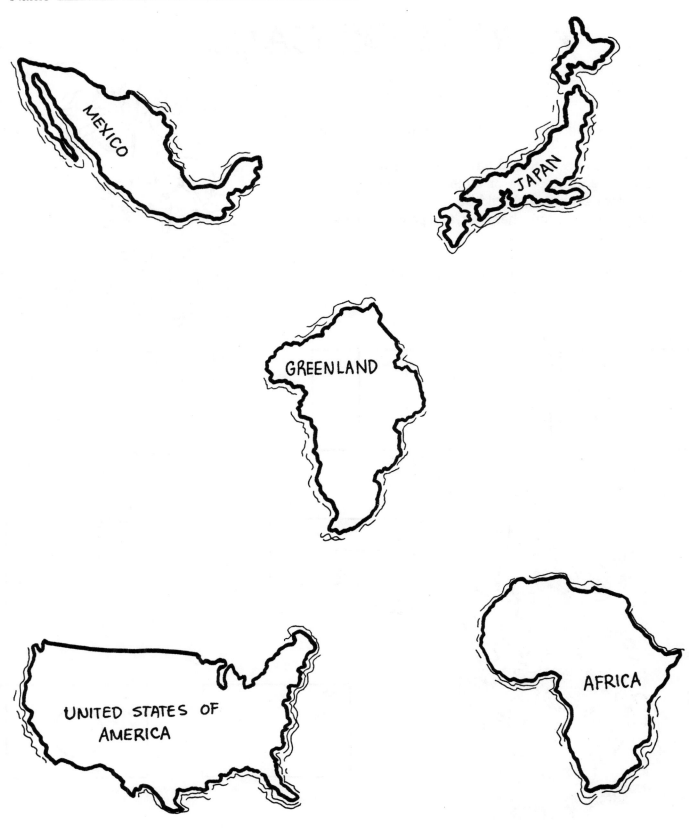

MEXICO

JAPAN

GREENLAND

UNITED STATES OF
AMERICA

AFRICA

Encyclopedia skills
© 1989 by Incentive Publications, Inc., Nashville, TN.

Answers on page 240.

PORT OF CALL

A ship's flag tells what country is the ship's home port.

The ships on page 203 have lost their flags.

Use an encyclopedia or almanac to find out what colors each flag should be.

Color the flags, cut them out, and paste them on the correct ships on page 203.

Draw and color the flag of your country.

My country's flag

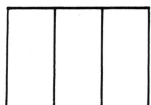

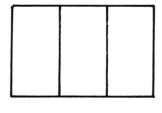

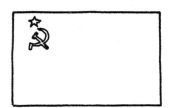

Encyclopedia/almanac skills
© 1989 by Incentive Publications, Inc., Nashville, TN.

Name _____

France

Italy

Argentina

MY COUNTRY

SOVIET UNION

China

Japan

Encyclopedia/almanac skills
© 1989 by Incentive Publications, Inc., Nashville, TN.

Answers on page 240.

THE AMAZING ALMANAC

An almanac is a reference book filled with all kinds of interesting facts.
Use an almanac to help you label the following.

1. Highest mountain in the United States

_____

2. Earth's largest continent

_____

3. World's longest river

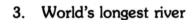

4. Largest island in the Atlantic

_____

5. Longest day of this year

_____

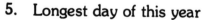

6. Lowest point on the earth

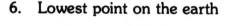

Answers on page 240.

Name _____

SAHARA SCENE

Write a sentence that explains each word below.
Use a dictionary for help.

1. nomad _____

2. caravan _____

3. oasis _____

In what part of the world would you find these things? _____

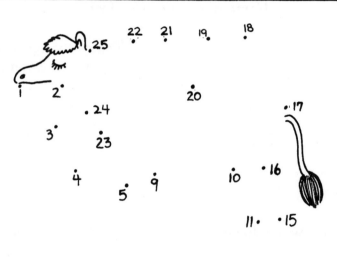

Connect the dots to find something that is very important to this part of the world.

BONUS:
1. How is this creature prepared for desert life? _____

_____

2. Some of these creatures have one hump and others have two. Name these two breeds and describe two differences between them. _____

_____

3. Where can you look to find the answers to these questions? _____

Answers on page 240.

Name _____

 # A GREAT PLACE TO LIVE!

A state picture map has the shape of the state and is filled with pictures that show
   what things are important in that state.
Use the space below to plan a picture map of your state or province.
Draw your state picture map on a separate sheet of paper.

(Hint: Use an encyclopedia and other reference books to gather information
   about your state.)

_____
Name of state or province

Animals that live here:

Things that grow on our land
and in our waters:

Jobs and occupations our people have:

Products we make in our factories:

Special places to visit:

Fun things to do here:

PICK THE PAGE

Table of Contents

On what page in this book can you find . . .

1. a story about a rabbit? ____

2. a story about baseball? ____

3. two poems? ____

4. the longest space story? ____

5. a story having a title with a pair of homonyms? ____

6. a poem that might be about a kangaroo? ____

7. a story about another planet? ____

8. a story that takes place on a farm? ____

9. a poem about an animal? ____

10. a story about a porcupine? ____

11. a story that *could* be about horseback riding? ____

12. the story or poem you'd most like to read? ____

Answers on page 240.

Name _____

✏ INFORMATION PLEASE!

Each person below needs one information source to complete his or her task.
Help each person decide where to look for help.
Write the proper source below each paper.

Spelling

speak
see
jump
~~pleeze~~

1. _____

Famous Americans
Name Born Died

Lincoln
Betsy Ross
Teddy Roosevelt

2. _____

SCIENCE
Which year, of the last three, had the highest temperature in July?

3. _____

Party Guests
Jack Dum   123-4900
Amy Kins
Pat Mee
Ima Bean
Josie Yo

4. _____

Mom,
    Please order a pair of sneakers and four skirts for me.
    Thanks,
    Thomasina

5. _____

Translation, Please!

• • • • • • • • •
• • • • • • • • •

6. _____

How far is it from New York to Washington D.C.?

7. _____

In what ocean are the Hawaiian islands located?

8. _____

Danny,
When you get home, please make a dessert for dinner.
Love,
MOM

9. _____

map
catalog
code

graph or chart
encyclopedia
cookbook

dictionary
telephone directory
key

Information sources
© 1989 by Incentive Publications, Inc., Nashville, TN.

Answers on page 240.

SKY VIEW

If you looked out of an airplane window, you might see a scene like this.
Read the words above the picture.
Draw a line to connect each word to the correct part of the picture.

railroad   mountain   road   city   bridge   forest   river

Map skills
© 1989 by INCENTIVE PUBLICATIONS, Inc., Nashville, TN.

Answers on page 240.

SATURDAY FUN

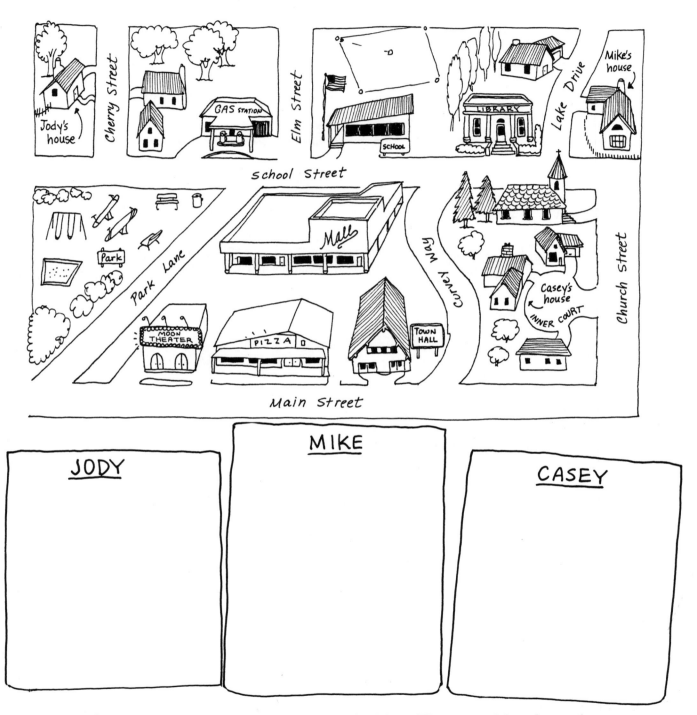

Jody, Mike and Casey want to go to a movie at the Moon Theater on Main Street, but none
of them knows how to get there.

Study the map above.

Make a set of directions for each boy to get him from his home to the theater.

Help the boys find their way home by drawing a line from the theater to each boy's home.

Map skills
© 1989 by Incentive Publications, Inc., Nashville, TN

Answers on page 240.

Name _____

THE EYES HAVE IT

1. Count the people in your class who have blue eyes.
   Color that many squares on the line graph labeled blue.

2. Count the people in your class who have brown eyes.
   Color that many squares on the line graph labeled brown.

3. Count the people in your class who have green eyes.
   Color that many squares on the line graph labeled green.

4. Count all of the remaining people in your class.
   Color that many squares on the line graph labeled other.

A graph is a picture that shows the relationship between two or more things.

Which color of eyes is most common in your class? _____

Which color is least common in your class? _____

```
        1   2   3   4   5   6   7   8   9   10  11  12  13  14  15  16  17
blue:  [ ][ ][ ][ ][ ][ ][ ][ ][ ][ ][ ][ ][ ][ ][ ][ ][ ]

brown: [ ][ ][ ][ ][ ][ ][ ][ ][ ][ ][ ][ ][ ][ ][ ][ ][ ]

green: [ ][ ][ ][ ][ ][ ][ ][ ][ ][ ][ ][ ][ ][ ][ ][ ][ ]

other: [ ][ ][ ][ ][ ][ ][ ][ ][ ][ ][ ][ ][ ][ ][ ][ ][ ]
```

Graphs/following directions
© 1989 by Incentive Publications, Inc., Nashville, TN.

211

Name _____

✏ CONTINENTAL COLOR CODE

The world has seven large areas of land called *continents*.
Most of the earth's surface is water.
Use the color key below to color this world map.

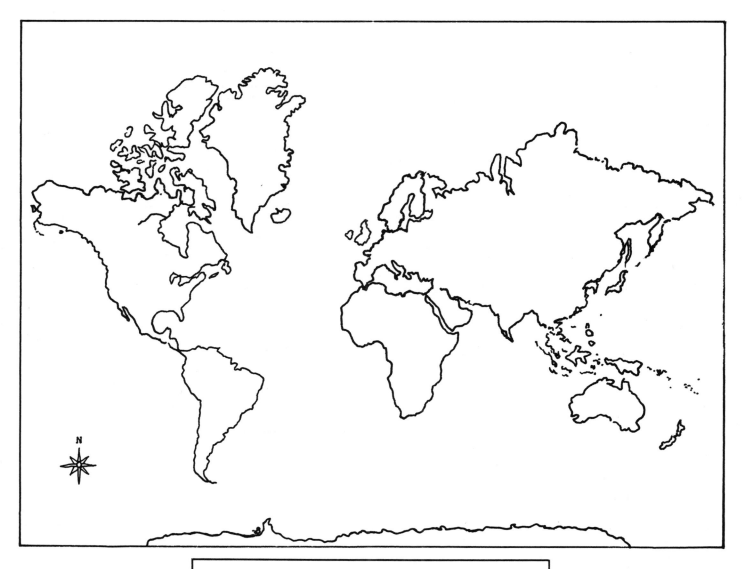

Color Key:

North America - red   Australia - brown
South America - green   Antarctica - white
Europe - orange   Asia - yellow
Africa - purple   Oceans - blue

Using a key
© 1989 by Incentive Publications, Inc., Nashville, TN.

Answers on page 240.

Name _____

KEEPING TRACK OF TRACKS

Wouldn't it be fun to discover tracks like these in the snow, mud or sand?
Cut out the animals and paste each animal beside its set of tracks.
Use the key as a guide.

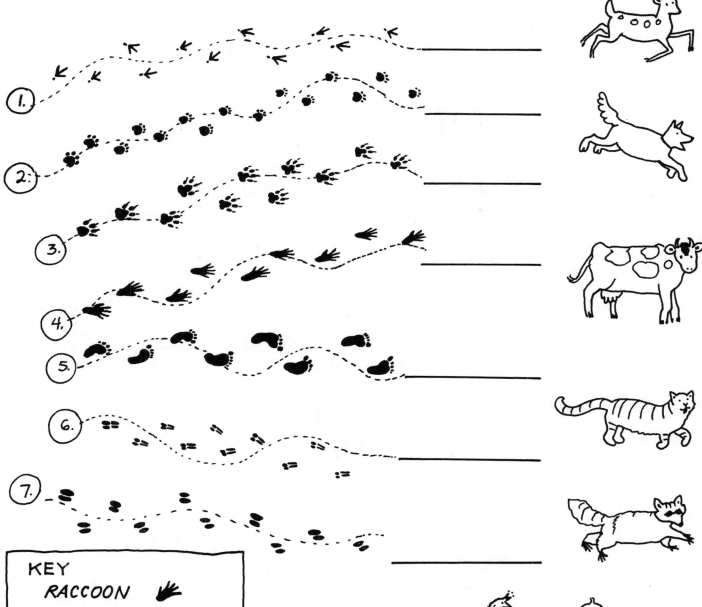

1. _____

2. _____

3. _____

4. _____

5. _____

6. _____

7. _____

KEY
RACCOON
COW
WHITE TAIL DEER
DOG
HUMAN BABY
HOUSE CAT
PHEASANT

Answers on page 240.

Using a key
© 1989 by Incentive Publications, Inc., Nashville, TN.

213

🍎 WAVE YOUR FLAGS!

SKILL: Decoding/encoding

PREPARATION:
- Make a copy of the International Flag Alphabet Key (below) for each student.
- Make a copy of the following student page for each student.

PROCEDURE:
1. Give each student one copy of the flag key and the student page.
2. Discuss the meanings of the words *code, decode,* and *encode.*
3. Ask the students to follow the directions on the student page to complete the decoding and encoding tasks.

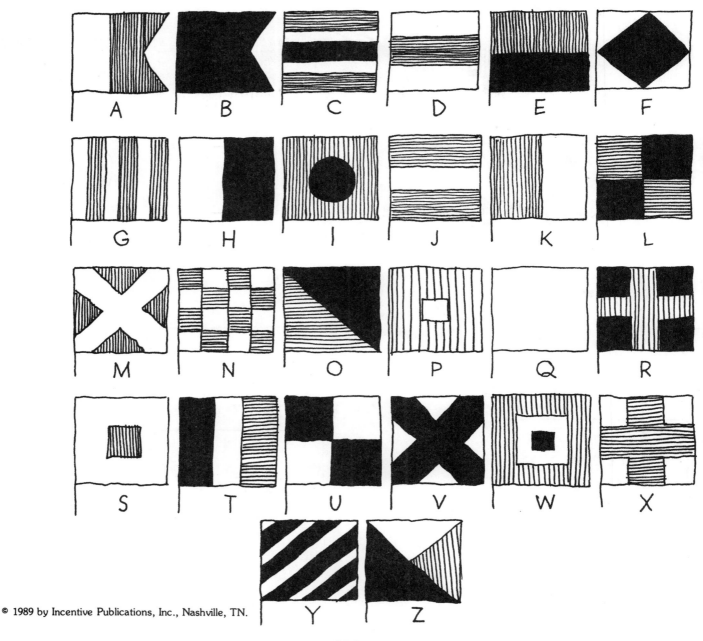

Name _____

WAVE YOUR FLAGS!

Use the International Flag Alphabet Key to decode the message below.
Write the correct letter below each flag.

Write the message here: _____ .

Encode your name in flags below!

Decoding/encoding
© 1989 by Incentive Publications, Inc., Nashville, TN.

Answers on page 240.

Name _____

WHAT'S A SNUFFLEGUMP?

Have you ever met a Snufflegump?

A Snufflegump has a round, furry face, a pointed nose, and teeth that look like tiny shovels. Its eyes are wide and wild looking. It has two long ears that hang down the sides of its head. A Snufflegump has a plump body with a heart-shaped bellybutton and a raggedy tail. It has four flat feet with three hairy toes on each. The Snufflegump likes to eat lilies, lizards, and lollipops for lunch!

Draw a Snufflegump in the space below.
Follow the description carefully.

Compare your drawing with those of your classmates to see who has followed the description the closest.
Whose Snufflegump is the funniest?

Following directions
© 1989 by Incentive Publications, Inc., Nashville, TN.

SHAPES CHARADE

SKILL: Following directions/planning

PREPARATION:
- Make a copy of the following two student pages for each student.
- Each student will need scissors, glue, crayons, and two sheets of white paper.

PROCEDURE:
1. Ask the students to read and follow the instructions on the student page to plan and create two "fantasy" figures.
2. Let the students share their creations with one another. Ask several students to explain to the class how they planned their creative figures.

SHAPES CHARADE

1. Color and cut out all of the shapes below and on page 219.
2. Use as many of the shapes as you wish to create a "fantasy" house. You can make a palace, a teepee, an igloo, a space capsule, an underwater or treetop home, or other dwelling!
3. Plan your creation carefully by arranging the shapes on a sheet of white paper. Move the shapes around until you are happy with the picture and then paste them in place.
4. Use leftover shapes to create a funny animal on another sheet of paper.

Name _____

✏ MIXED-UP MENU

These foods are all mixed up!
Complete the outline below to organize the foods.

cream of tomato
SHREDDED WHEAT
ice cream sundae
tart
MILK
SCRAMBLED EGGS
Turkey
fried eggs
HAM & CHEESE
vegetable beef
cream puff
Jell-O
donuts
rice flakes
COLA
CORN FLAKES
POACHED EGGS
oatmeal
water
ORANGE JUICE
CHOCOLATE PUDDING
MUFFINS
chicken noodle
PEANUT BUTTER + JELLY

BREAKFAST MENU

I. Eggs
A _____
B _____
C _____

II. Cereals
A _____
B _____
C _____
D _____

III. Pastries
A _____
B _____
C _____
D _____

LUNCH MENU

I. Sandwiches
A _____
B _____
C _____

II. Soups
A _____
B _____
C _____

III. Desserts
A _____
B _____
C _____

IV. Drinks
A _____
B _____
C _____
D _____

Outlines
© 1989 by Incentive Publications, Inc., Nashville, TN.

Answers on page 240.

APPENDIX

ANTONYMS

above - below
absent - present
add - subtract
after - before
alike - different
all - none
always - never
ancient - modern
awake - asleep
back - front
backward - forward
bad - good
beautiful - ugly
begin - end
big - little
buy - sell
city - country
close - open
cold - hot
come - go
cool - warm
cry - laugh
danger - safety
dark - light
dead - alive
deep - shallow
dirty - clean
dry - wet
early - late
easy - hard
empty - full
fast - slow

fat - thin
first - last
funny - serious
give - take
great - small
happy - sad
hard - soft
here - there
in - out
inside - outside
lead - follow
light - heavy
live - die
long - short
loud - soft
love - hate
low - high
many - few
more - less
narrow - wide
near - far
new - old
night - day
no - yes
noisy - quiet
polite - rude
powerful - weak
push - pull
question - answer
raise - lower
real - fake
remember - forget

rich - poor
right - left
right - wrong
rough - smooth
same - different
scream - whisper
slow - fast
small - large
smile - frown
speak - listen
stand - sit
stop - start
tight - loose
to - from
top - bottom
true - false
weak - strong
well - ill
wild - tame
won - lost
you - I
young - old

HOMONYMS

air - heir	hole - whole	sale - sail
aisle - isle	in - inn	sea - see
altar - alter	knows - nose	seem - seam
ate - eight	leak - leek	seen - scene
bare - bear	led - lead	sell - cell
be - bee	loan - lone	sent - scent - cent
beach - beech	made - maid	sew - sow - so
beat - beet	male - mail	shear - sheer
blue - blew	meat - meet	slay - sleigh
bore - boar	miner - minor	some - sum
bow - bough	morning - mourning	son - sun
break - brake	naval - navel	sore - soar
bridal - bridle	need - knead	stare - stair
bury - berry	night - knight	stationary - stationery
buy - by- bye	new - knew - gnu	steak - stake
capitol - capital	no - know	steal - steel
cereal - serial	none - nun	straight - strait
coarse - course	not - knot	tacks - tax
creak - creek	our - hour	tale - tail
dear - deer	pain - pane	tea - tee
dew - do	pair - pare - pear	there - their
die - dye	pale - pail	threw - through
fair - fare	peace - piece	to - too - two
feat - feet	plane - plain	tow - toe
flea - flee	pray - prey	vain - vein - vane
flower - flour	presents - presence	wade - weighed
four - for	principal - principle	wait - weight
fourth - forth	rain - rein	waste - waist
fur - fir	read - reed	way - weigh
great - grate	real - reel	weak - week
groan - grown	red - read	won - one
hangar - hanger	ring - wring	wood - would
hare - hair	road - rode	wrap - rap
haul - hall	roomer - rumor	write - right
heal - heel	root - route	you - ewe
here - hear	rows - rose	

© 1989 by Incentive Publications, Inc., Nashville, TN.

WORDS
THAT CONFUSE

accept (receive), **except** (exclude)
advise (to give advice), **advice** (counsel)
affect (to influence), **effect** (result)
already (previously), **all ready** (completely prepared)
capital (seat of government), **capitol** (building)
choose (select), **chose** (selected)
desert (dry, sandy region; to abandon), **dessert** (food)
holy (sacred), **holey (having holes), wholly** (totally)
its (belonging to), **it's** (it is, it has)
knew (was acquainted with, was aware of), **new** (current)
lay (to put or place), **lie** (to recline)
led (guided), **lead** (to guide, metallic chemical element)
lose (misplace), **loose** (free, unbound)
medal (award for action or merit), **metal** (any of a class of chemical elements)
peace (freedom from war), **piece** (part, section)
presents (gifts), **presence** (existence, attendance)
principal (chief, head), **principle** (basic law or truth)
quite (completely, entirely), **quiet** (still, hushed), **quit** (to free oneself of)
raise (lift, elevate), **rise** (to stand)
read (to interpret characters and symbols of printed matter), **red** (primary color)
scene (setting), **seen** (has viewed)
sit (to rest the body on the buttocks with the torso upright), **set** (to put or place something),
  sat (past tense of sit)
stationery (writing materials), **stationary** (immovable)
their (belonging to them), **there** (at or in that place), **they're** (they are)
through (from end to end), **though** (in spite of), **thought** (act or process of thinking)
trough (container for holding water or food for animals), **tough** (strong but pliant)
wait (remain), **weight** (heaviness)
waste (to destroy), **waist** (part of body between ribs and hips)
wear (to have on the body), **where** (in or at what place)
whole (intact), **hole** (cavity)
whose (that or those belonging to whom), **who's** (who is, who has)

© 1989 by Incentive Publications, Inc., Nashville, TN.

READING BULLETIN BOARD

WHAT TO USE:
- construction paper (royal colors such as purple, blue, red & yellow)
- scissors
- crayons or markers
- stapler
- tape

WHAT TO DO:
Construct a bulletin board like the one shown above. Use the board as a showcase for students' book reviews, or motivate students to read by displaying book jackets and brief reviews of the books.

WRITING BULLETIN BOARD

On the easel:
- leafy hideouts
- a giggling brook
- wispy clouds swept by angel brooms
- mounds of purple velvet mountains
- hot sizzling sounds
- cotton-ball clouds
- sunflowers with up-turned faces
- softly purring balls of fur
- flashes of color
- chocolate rivers and strawberry pools
- glassy stare-back eyes

MEET THE WORD ARTISTS !

WHAT TO USE:
- construction paper
- scissors
- crayons or markers
- stapler
- tape

WHAT TO DO:
Construct a bulletin board like the one shown above. Instruct each student to choose one or more descriptive phrases from the easel and to use them in a brief paragraph that "draws a picture" of an object, scene, or event. Display the students' paragraphs on the board.

STUDY SKILLS BULLETIN BOARD

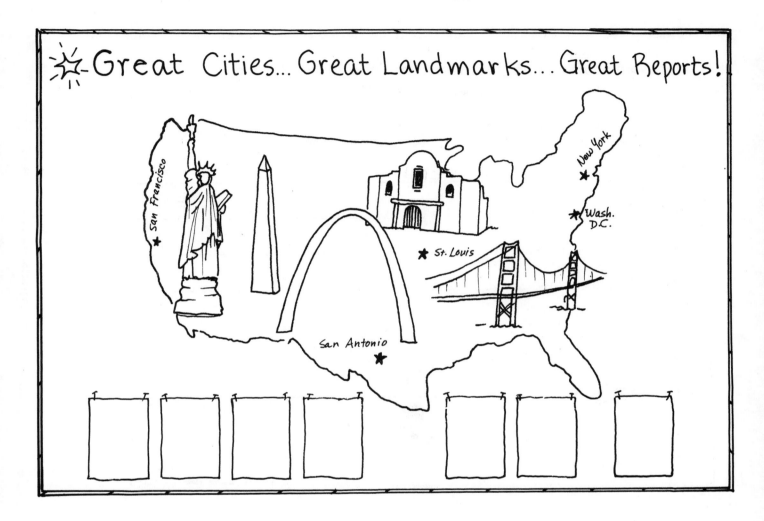

WHAT TO USE:

- construction paper
- crayons or markers
- scissors
- thumbtacks
- stapler
- tape
- yarn

WHAT TO DO:

Construct a bulletin board like the one shown above. Place stars on the map to show the locations of these cities: Washington D.C., New York City, St. Louis, San Francisco, and San Antonio. Attach large cutouts of these famous "landmarks" to the map (not beside their locations): the Washington Monument, the Statue of Liberty, the Golden Gate Bridge, the Alamo, and the Gateway Arch. Let the students use strings of yarn and thumbtacks to connect each landmark to its location. Ask the students to use reference books to write brief reports about each landmark. Display the reports on the bulletin board.

Name _____

 CLUE ME IN

Finish these sentences to help your teacher find books that you like and plan activities that are interesting to you.
There are no right or wrong answers, and there will be no grade.
No one will see this paper except your teacher.

Do not think about your answers too long.
Answer each question before going on to the next one.

1. School is _____ .

2. The thing I like best at school is _____ .

3. The thing I like least at school is _____ .

4. I think books are _____ .

5. I like to read about _____ .

6. I don't like books that _____ .

7. I wish my teacher _____

_____ .

8. I wish my classmates _____

_____ .

9. I think the principal _____

_____ .

10. I like my friends to _____

_____ .

11. I don't like my friends to _____

_____ .

12. I'm glad I _____

_____ .

Name _____

13. I wish I could _____

_____ .

14. I am happy when _____

_____ .

15. I am unhappy when _____

_____ .

16. At home I like to _____

_____ .

17. I worry about _____

_____ .

18. I really get angry when _____

_____ .

19. I'd like school better if _____

_____ .

20. My favorite television program is _____ .

21. When I grow up _____

_____ .

22. I wish someone would help me _____

_____ .

23. On Saturdays I _____

_____ .

24. My favorite book is _____ .

25. If I ran the school _____

_____ .

TWENTY-TWO FUN THINGS TO DO TO MAKE BOOKS COME ALIVE FOR YOUNG READERS

1. Help the students make bookmarks illustrating story characters to accompany a "read-aloud" book.

2. Prepare felt-board characters and background scenery to "present" a book to the class on a felt board.

3. Provide the class with a variety of good picture books. Ask each student to select a book to share with a child from a foreign country who speaks another language or a very young child who has not learned to read.

4. Secure multiple copies of a favorite book. Ask the students to illustrate the happiest, funniest, or saddest part of the book. Mount the illustrations on a bulletin board so that the students may discuss and compare their illustrations.

5. Have the students make puppets from felt or corduroy. Gather a large assortment of buttons, yarn, markers, etc. for the students to use in turning the puppets into characters from a favorite story. Let the students use the puppets to present the story.

6. Provide the students with paper bags, half-pint cartons or socks to use in designing original puppets for original stories!

7. Hand out copies of an attractive reading record for a "last day of school" surprise. Ask the students to record vacation reading on their reading records and to present the reading records to their new teachers at the beginning of the next school year.

8. Tell stories often. Practice refining your own special versions of class favorites.

9. Help the class plan and paint background scenery to be used in dramatizing a special book.

10. Appoint student committees to select books from the library for the classroom reading corner before holidays and other special occasions.

11. Provide the students with art supplies to be used in making life-size characters from chosen books. Students should trace around each other on butcher paper, draw the features of the characters on the outlines, and cut out the figures. Stage a "book parade" by taping the character cutouts on the classroom wall!

12. Sponsor a "read in"! Set aside a time each day for free-choice reading. Provide the students with lots of books and allow each student to choose what he or she would like to read — no strings attached!

13. Ask the students to write three or four-line book reviews to be published in a class newspaper.

14. Ask each student to select one book to share with a friend. Allow time for the sharing!

15. Ask each student to select the one book that he or she would take on a long, long journey if he or she could take only one book. Discuss the selected books and the reasons for the selections.

A BOOK IS A FRIEND FOREVER

16. Make mobiles to hang from the ceiling to "advertise" new books.

17. Feature a "how-to" book each week by having a class activity period based on instruction from the book.

18. Have the students use a variety of art materials and many sizes of cardboard boxes to make dioramas illustrating interesting scenes from books.

19. Have a "guess what book I am" session. Students may portray favorite book characters through costuming and creative dramatics. (Remind the students to choose books that can be identified easily by the portrayal of one character.)

20. Write five clues about each of several books on strips of paper. Put the clues in small, flat boxes. Write the name of the book on the bottom of the box. Instruct a student to select a box, open it, and draw one clue at a time. The student may continue drawing clues until he or she identifies the book or until all of the clues have been read. If the student identifies the book, he or she may choose another box. Otherwise, the student may find the answer on the bottom of the box and allow another student to take the next turn.

21. Help the students make a classroom movie. Instruct the students to draw or paint scenes from a story and paste the scenes on a roll of butcher paper attached to two broom handles. Place the broom handles in holes cut in a cardboard box theater and "roll" the paper to show the movie.

22. Have each student write a brief review of a book he or she would like to nominate for "book of the week." Deliver the reviews to the librarian who will select the winner based on the nominations.

Name _____

READING RECORD

Date	Title Of Book	Pages	New Words

✏ THIS IS MY WEEK

Name _____

	What I did today	My Homework Plan
Monday		
Tuesday		
Wednesday		
Thursday		
Friday		

Comments:

Other **KIDS' STUFF**™ books for Primary Grades
Language Arts and Reading

Farnette, Cherrie; Forte, Imogene and Loss, Barbara. **Something Special.** 1982.
   - word identification, word usage and comprehension units with reproducible pages coded for three levels of difficulty.

Farnette, Cherrie; Forte, Imogene and Harris Loss, Barbara. **Special Kids' Stuff, Rev. Ed. 1989.**
   - word identification, word usage and comprehension units with reproducible pages coded for three levels of difficulty.

Forte, Imogene. **Library & Reference Bulletin Boards.** 1986.
   - motivational bulletin boards with patterns and additional captions.

Forte, Imogene. **Read About It Primary Grades.** 1982.
   - reproducible activities which focus on word recognition, word usage and independent reading skills.

Forte, Imogene. **Skillstuff: Reading.** 1979.
   - word recognition and usage, comprehension and study skills.

Forte, Imogene. **Think About It Primary Grades.** 1981.
   - reproducible activity sheets designed to develop thinking skills such as discovering, predicting, inventing, interpreting, imagining and more.

Forte, Imogene. **Write About It Primary Grades.** 1983.
   - reproducible work sheets which focus on vocabulary development, technical writing, composition and original writing.

Forte, Imogene and Pangle, Mary Ann. **Reading Bulletin Boards.** 1986.
   - includes skills-based activities to supplement daily reading programs.

Frank, Marjorie. **Complete Writing Lessons For The Primary Grades.** 1987.
   - motivating writing lessons which include starter activities, writing instructions, presentation and follow-up ideas, and reproducible student pages.

Frank, Marjorie. **If You're Trying To Teach Kids How To Write, You've Gotta Have This Book.** 1979.
   - a how-to book for understanding and working with the whole writing process with ideas for specific activities and suggestions for solving writing problems.

Grubb, Jan. **The Media Mouse Collection of Awards & Incentives.** 1988.
   - reproducible awards, bookmarks, displays and games to encourage library/media center skills and enthusiasm.

Reading Yellow Pages For Students and Teachers. 1988.
   - a book of reference lists for teaching basic reading skills.

Richards, Joanne and Standley, Marianne. **One For The Books.** 1984.
   - original and creative ways to present book reports.

Richards, Joanne and Standley, Marianne. **Write Here.** 1984.
   - includes writing activities, bulletin boards and suggestions for motivating students.

The Students' Book of Lists, Rev. Ed. 1988.
   - lists of people, places, and things for research, reports, homework, skills drills, etc.

Writing Yellow Pages For Students and Teachers. 1988.
   - a book of reference lists for teaching basic writing skills.

105 CLASSICS
FOR YOUNG READERS

Alexander and the Terrible, Horrible, No Good, Very Bad Day, Viorst; Macmillan.

The Alligator with the Lean, Mean Smile, Nordlight; Scholastic.

Amelia Bedelia, Parish; Greenwillow.

And to Think That I Saw It on Mulberry Street, Seuss; Houghton Mifflin.

Baseball Fever, Hurwitz; Morrow/Dell.

Bedtime for Frances, Hoban; Harper & Row.

Blueberries for Sal, McCloskey; Viking.

Bridge to Terabithia, Paterson; Crowell.

The Cat in the Hat, Seuss; Random House.

Charlotte's Web, E.B. White; Harper & Row.

Clifford the Big Red Dog, Bridwell; Scholastic.

The Clown of God, DePaola; Harcourt Brace Jovanovich.

Corduroy, Freeman; Viking.

The Cricket in Times Square, Selden; Dell.

Curious George, Rey; Houghton Mifflin.

Dandelion, Freeman; Viking.

Danny and the Dinosaur, Hoff; Harper & Row.

Danny, The Champion of the World, Dahl; Knopf, Alfred A., Inc.

A Dark, Dark Tale, Brown; Dial.

The Day Jimmy's Boa Ate The Wash, Noble; Dial.

Dreams, Spier; Doubleday.

Eloise, Thompson; Simon & Schuster.

Emma's Vacation, McPhail; Dutton.

The Enormous Egg, Butterworth; Little, Brown & Co.

The Enormous Crocodile, Dahl; Knoph, Alfred A., Inc.

Family Farm, Coclar; Dial.

A Fly Went By, McClintock; Random House.

Frog and Toad Together, Lobel; Harper & Row.

Gentle Ben, Morey; Dutton.

The Giving Tree, Silverstein; Harper & Row.

Green Eggs and Ham, Seuss; Random House.

Harold and the Purple Crayon, Johnson; Harper & Row.

Harry, The Dirty Dog, Zion; Harper & Row.

Heidi, Spyri; Macmillan.

Helen Keller, Graff; Garrard.

Homer Price, McCloskey; Viking.

Horton Hatches the Egg, Seuss; Random House.

How the Grinch Stole Christmas, Seuss; Random House.

How To Eat Fried Worms, Rockwell; Watts/Dell.

I Can Read With My Eyes Shut, Seuss; Random House.

If I Ran the Zoo, Seuss; Random House.

If You Give a Mouse a Cookie, Numeroff; Harper & Row.

I'll Fix Anthony, Viorst; Harper & Row.

I'll Teach My Dog 100 Words, Seuss; Random House.

In A People House, Seuss; Random House.

Incredible Journey, Burnford; Little/Bantam.

Ira Sleeps Over, Waber; Houghton Mifflin.

Katy and the Big Snow, Burton; Houghton Mifflin.

Keep the Lights Burning, Abbie, Roop; Carolrhoda Books.

King of the Wind, Henry; Random House.

Least of All, Purdy; Macmillan.

Leo, The Late Bloomer, Krauss; Windmill.

The Little House, Burton; Houghton Mifflin.

Little House on the Prairie, Wilder; Harper & Row.

The Little Island, MacDonald/ Weisgard; Doubleday.

Lyle, Lyle Crocodile, Waber; Houghton Mifflin.

Madeline, Bemelmans; Viking.

Make Way for Ducklings, McCloskey; Viking.

The Mare on the Hill, Locker; Dial.

Mary Poppins, Travers; Buccaneer.

The Midnight Farm, Lindbergh; Dial.

Millions of Cats, Gag; Coward.

Miss Nelson Is Missing, Allard; Houghton Mifflin.

The Mountain That Loved a Bird, McLerran; Picture Book Studio.

Mouse Tales, Lobel; Harper & Row.

Mr. Popper's Penguins, Atwater; Little, Brown & Co.

The Napping House, Wood; Harcourt Brace Jovanovich.

Nate the Great, Sharmat; Coward.

The New Kid on the Block, Prelutsky; Greenwillow.

The Night Book, Strand; Crown.

Noah's Ark, Spier; Doubleday.

Nobody Listens To Andrew, Guilfoile; Follett.

Norman the Doorman, Freeman; Viking.

Nose for Trouble, Kjelgaard; Holiday/Bantam.

Oh, Were They Ever Happy, Spier; Doubleday.

Old Henry, Blos; Morrow.

The One in the Middle Is the Green Kangaroo, Blume; Dell.

One Morning in Maine, McCloskey; Viking.

Only the Cat Saw, Wolff; Dodd, Mead.

The Polar Express, Van Allsburg; Houghton Mifflin.

Pumpkin, Pumpkin, Titherington; Greenwillow.

Ralph S. Mouse, Zelinsky; Morrow.

Ramona Quimby, Age 8, Cleary; Morrow/Dell.

Reflections, Jonas; Greenwillow.

The Relatives Came, Rylant; Bradbury.

The Secret Three, Myrick; Harper & Row.

The Selfish Giant, Wilde; Picture Book Studio.

Sheep in a Jeep, Shaw; Houghton Mifflin.

Sometimes I Dance Mountains, Baylor; Scribner.

Stone Soup, McGovern; Scribner.

Story About Ping, Flack; Viking.

Strawberry Girl, Lenski; Lippincott/Dell.

Stuart Little, White; Harper & Row.

The Tenth Good Thing About Barney, Gackenbach; Seabury.

The Town Mouse and the Country Mouse, Aesop/Stevens; Holiday.

The Treasure, Shulevitz; Farrar, Strauss & Giroux.

The Trumpet of the Swan, White; Harper & Row.

The Vegetable Thieves, Moore; Viking.

The Velveteen Rabbit, Williams; Holt, Rinehart & Winston.

The Very Hungry Caterpillar, Carle; Collins World.

The Westing Game, Raskin; Avon.

When I Was Young in the Mountains, Rylant; Bradbury.

When the Boys Ran the House, Carris; Harper & Row Jr. Books.

Where the Wild Things Are, Sendak; Harper & Row.

The Wreck of the Zephyr, Van Allsburg; Houghton Mifflin.

ANSWER KEY

Pg. 39 Saturday, help, can, jump, city, pet, went, thing, laugh, big, fish, had, family

Pg. 40 guess, cane, name, know, high, friend, like, laugh, tail, year, horse, something

Pg. 54 1) playing 2) dressing 3) dolls 4) tallest 5) smaller 6) wanted 7) girls 8) walked 9) slowly

Pg. 56 I love to listen to stories. Can you write one for me?

Pg. 57 1) wildly 2) mighty 3) excitement 4) storm 5) settled 6) loud 7) wandering 8) night 9) opened 10) old 11) soaked 12) poor 13) found 14) full 15) afraid 16) help 17) kind 18) in 19) shelter 20) welcome

Pg. 70 1) spring-like, warm and cheerful, bright and beautiful 2) eerie, scary, dark and stormy 3) icy and snowy, shivery, winter wonderland

Pg. 78 1) three 2) two 3) boots 4) apple 5) three 6) umbrella 7) answers will vary

Pg. 86 1) merrily 2) joyful 3) sparkling 4) golden 5) brilliant 6) breathtaking 7) sweet

Pg. 88 Items that do not need to be hung to dry: thermos of tea, scissors, apple, needles, purse.

Pg. 90 Country Scene: tractor, cow, barn, farmer
City Scene: bus, office building, hot dog vendor, taxi

Pg. 100

Pg. 104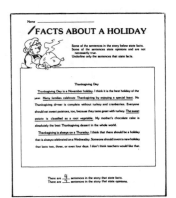

Pg. 124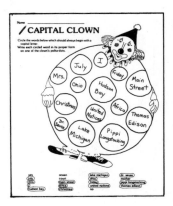

Pg. 125 A) 3. 5. 9. B) 1. 4. 6. 10. C) 2. 7. 8

Pg. 126 Perfect Letters: Professor U.R. Smart, Miss Sara Frank, President George Washington, Rev. Hal Hanks.

M.C. Rice Apt. 22 55 Pigeon Rd. Dallas, Texas	Miss Hansel Hook 444 Cedar Street Gary, Indiana	Mrs. Bob Boots 98 Bunny Trail Rd. Columbia, TN
Richard T. Jennings Old Tower Trail Rt. 2 Ely, Minnesota	Mr. Steve Potts 3636 High Point Circle Durham, North Carolina	Dr. John Kit 233 Elm St. Grover, IL
Mr. Ben Hays 804 Water Street Boston, MA	Miss Beth Jackson 66 River Run Lansing, Michigan	Mr. I.M. Bigg 220 Large Lake Lane Topeka, Kansas

Pg. 127 can't, aren't, she'll, we're, won't, you've, I'm, let's, he's, we'd, they're, here's, hadn't, we've, who'd

Pg. 133 Nouns: lady, king, leader, prince, ruler, jester, snob, queen

Pg. 136 Proper Nouns: Sam, Florida, Bozo, Disneyland, New York, Captain Cook
Common Nouns: planet, boat, island, dog, street, church
Note: Common and proper noun "synonyms" will vary.

Pg. 141   *Nouns:* turkeys, horns, princes, frogs, girls, boys, dinosaurs, snails, sodas, lizards, lollipops
Verbs: honk, kiss, bother, dance, slurping, lick   *Adverbs:* loudly, really, daintily, lazily
Adjectives: ten, handsome, giggly, nine, silly

Pg. 143   1) bell 2) nut 3) web 4) bus 5) lamp 6) nest 7) pig 8) drum 9) mask

Pg. 145   1) snowy day 2) cloudy day 3) sunny day 4) stormy day 5) cold day 6) foggy day 7) dark day
8) windy day 9) rainy day 10) hot day

Pg. 197   1) BABY - ball, balloon, banana, barn, bat, bathtub, bear - BEAVER 2) BED - bee, beet, bell, bib, bicycle - BIRD
3) BLOCKS-boat, bone, book, bottle, bow, bowl - BOX 4) BRIDE - bridge, bubble, buggy, bull, burglar, bus - BUTTERFLY

Pg. 198   1) units of measure   2) cities in the U.S.   3) rivers   4) musical instruments   5) inventors   6) gardening tools
7) athletes   8) countries   9) artists   10) geometric figures   11) U.S. Presidents   12) provinces of Canada
13) oceans 14) cities in Australia Bonus: famous "firsts" - first U.S. President, first man on the moon, first man and
woman, first female Supreme Court Justice

Pg. 199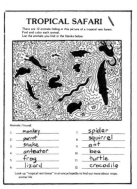

Pg. 201

Pg. 203

Pg. 204   1) Mount McKinley 2) Asia 3) Amazon 4) Greenland 5) June 21 or 22 (varies year to year)
6) Marina Trench (Pacific Ocean)

Pg. 205   Asian or African deserts   1) Can replace rapidly water lost from body,
stores fat in its hump(s), can close its nostrils, has heavy protective
eyelashes. 2) Dromedaries - 1 hump Bactrian camels - 2 humps
Bactrian camels are shorter and heavier and do not have to live in the
desert like dromedaries. 3) encyclopedia

Pg. 207   1) 11 2) 69 3) 94 4) 45 5) 20 6) 16 7) 45 8) 28 9) 94 10) 3 11) 82 12) answer will vary

Pg. 208   1) dictionary 2) encyclopedia 3) graph or chart 4) telephone directory 5) catalog 6) code 7) key 8) map
9) cookbook

Pg. 209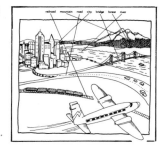

Pg. 210

Directions may vary.

Pg. 212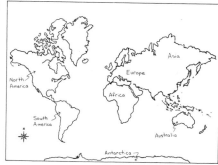

Pg. 213   1) pheasant 2) house cat 3) dog 4) raccoon 5) human baby 6) whitetail deer 7) cow

Pg. 215   Message: You are special

Pg. 220   BREAKFAST I. scrambled eggs, fried eggs, poached eggs II. rice flakes, shredded wheat, corn flakes, oatmeal III. tart,
cream puff, donuts, muffins LUNCH I. ham and cheese, peanut butter and jelly, turkey II. vegetable beef, chicken
noodle, cream of tomato III. ice cream sundae, chocolate pudding, Jell-O IV. cola, milk, orange juice, water